THE ABILITIES OF YOUNG CHILDREN

RUTH GRIFFITHS, O.B.E.

THE ABILITIES OF
YOUNG CHILDREN

A COMPREHENSIVE SYSTEM
OF
MENTAL MEASUREMENT
FOR
THE FIRST EIGHT YEARS OF LIFE

BY

RUTH GRIFFITHS
O.B.E., M.A., Ph.D., etc.

Author of
The Abilities of Babies
Imagination in Early Childhood, etc.

CHILD DEVELOPMENT RESEARCH CENTRE
LONDON

CHILD DEVELOPMENT RESEARCH CENTRE
47 Hollycroft Avenue, London, N.W.3.

Printed in Great Britain by
YOUNG AND SON (PRINTERS) LTD., CHARD, SOMERSET

PREFACE

THE mental tests to be described in this volume began to come into being several years ago, after the publication of my book, "The Abilities of Babies". It early became obvious that this scale of tests would be more useful if extended upwards and thus made available for testing somewhat older children. In child guidance work for example, it is the pre-school children, and the youngest of school children, for whom this approach would seem to be most helpful.

In the past clinical psychologists have not often been called upon to deal with testing the intelligence or mental development of little babies, which has been largely in the hands of the medical officers who use Gesell's tests and other American scales. Thus children of the next age group from about 2 to 8 years, are more frequently referred to child guidance centres, and need to be assessed for one reason or another by the clinical psychologist. The profile technique to be described in this book would appear to be the appropriate method to use for children of these ages.

The work of extending the scale upwards to this next age group, has been lengthy and time consuming, and has occupied many years of entirely voluntary work. The need for such a technique is clearly exemplified when we consider in particular the problems of young cerebral palsied children, young deaf children, little mongol children and others, all of whom may require to be assessed in infancy or early childhood if maximum benefit is to ensue. (See Chapter IX).

Medical officers and paediatricians who have been for many years familiar with the Terman Merrill and other tests, have welcomed this comprehensive approach to the mental testing of babies and very young children, and have also frequently asked that my tests should be extended beyond the first two years. This new volume of tests is therefore the result not only of a realisation of the needs of the children concerned, but is also the necessary and logical next step in improving techniques, and making these available to other workers, in both the educational and mental health fields.

At the Child Development Research Centre courses of lectures, demonstrations and discussions of these methods, and their application, have been held since the publication of my book "The Abilities of Babies" in 1954. Up to the time of writing forty-one courses of lectures have been held here, and several hundred people, mainly psychologists and medical officers, have accepted this brief training in the new method of assessment.

From among these members of lecture courses I am indebted to many for their kindly interest in this lengthy research project of extending the scales up to the eighth year. In particular I must mention here and express my gratitude to the twelve psychologists and medical officers, who after studying the method at this centre or elsewhere undertook to test children to help increase the data for this research. Between them, with the kind acquiescence of their Authorities, they tested several hundred children for this project. This was a tremendous help to the investigator, who no longer found herself entirely alone to carry all this side of the work, and of course it also increased the numbers of test results available for the standardisation of the extended scales.

The names of the members of the team who helped in this way, giving frequently of their own time to the testing, and sometimes testing children in the various schools and centres where they worked, are given below:

Dr. O. N. Bywaters, M.B., B.S., Medical Officer for Dr. Barnado's Homes.

Miss M. T. Eaglesim, M.A., Ed.B., Principle Clinical Psychologist, Central Child Guidance Clinic, Glasgow.

Dr. G. N. Ellis, Medical Officer, Swansea Health Department.

Dr. E. F. Hunter, Glasgow Corporation, Health and Welfare Department.

Mrs. A. M. Jones, M.A., B.Ed., Clinical Psychologist, Whitchurch Hospital, Cardiff.

Miss M. L. Kerr, M.A., Ed.B., Senior Psychologist, Child Guidance Service, Glasgow.

Dr. J. R. Ludlow, M.B.E., Medical Officer, Kent County Council.

Miss E. Mitchell, M.A., Ed.B., Clinical Psychologist, Glasgow Clinic.

Miss A. Queenan, Ed.B., Psychologist, Glasgow Clinic.

Miss B. T. Skelsey, M.Sc., Psychologist, Wiltshire County Council and Chailey Heritage.

Miss Rose Unmack, M.A., Ph.D., Psychologist, The National Children's Home and St. George's Hospital.

Dr. A. G. Vallance, Medical Officer, Glasgow Corporation.

Our thanks are also due to Dr. B. H. Burne of Amersham for the colour photograph of the Apparatus that precedes Part III.

The kindness of all these friends in helping in the early stages of the work will not be forgotten.

My thanks are also due to those other psychologists and doctors who after studying the methods with us here, sent occasional test results for inclusion in the research. I must in particular mention Dr. Rose Unmack who not only herself carried out a considerable number of tests, but more recently has read the manuscript of this book, before publication, and has made several encouraging and helpful comments.

I also remember with gratitude those officers, teachers in the schools visited, parents who brought children to the Child Development Research Centre for testing, and many others who contributed directly or indirectly, to the progress of this work.

In conclusion I must thank very warmly at this time my partner, administrative assistant, and friend, Miss Vida Hume, M.A., who, for most of this lengthy period of years, lived and worked at the Child Development Research Centre, and gave most valuable assistance to me with all those routine tasks that are associated with the building up of the records, and in many other ways. She also kept in touch with the members of the research team during the years when we were gathering the data, keeping them supplied with the duplicated provisional record books, and with apparatus as needed. Her help throughout has been invaluable and in her retirement she is greatly missed.

RUTH GRIFFITHS.

47 Hollycroft Avenue,
London, N.W.3.
December, 1970.

CONTENTS

PART III

ADMINISTERING THE EXTENDED SCALES

LIST OF TABLES, FIGURES
AND PLATES

TABLES

x

PLATES

CHAPTER I

INTRODUCTION

THIS book has been planned primarily as a sequel to "The Abilities of Babies", first published in 1954[1], and now extends the diagnostic technique described in that earlier volume up to and including the eighth year of life.

The earlier tests, which dealt with the first two years only, have been used for many years by psychologists, medical officers, paediatricians, and others, in their work of mental assessment of babies and very young children. These professional workers have found the tests of value in clinical diagnosis in hospitals, clinics and welfare centres, and in private practice, with both normal and handicapped children of all groups. The method has also been used in researches of many kinds into the problems of infancy, with particular reference to mental and physical disabilities and handicaps.

Many requests have been received by the author during these past few years, for the extension of these tests, for use in clinical practice with somewhat older children; and the new tests of mental development to be described in the present volume, are the result of the realisation of the needs in the diagnostic situation of this next age group, that is the period from two years of age up to the eighth year. Thus children of nursery school and infant school ages, need to be catered for in this field of work, and it would appear evident that the profile[2] as a diagnostic tool, can throw light on many of the problems met with.

In this book therefore we shall describe this further research into test construction, which has had as its goal, the provision of a method calculated to help diagnosis of mental status in many conditions found among young children. The five-scale test described in "The Abilities of Babies", has been revised and also extended in the new scales, to cover the entire period from birth to eight years, and a sixth scale to be described later has been added. This sixth scale incorporates items of "practical reasoning", that cannot be measured

[1] "The Abilities of Babies", University of London Press, 1954, 1964, 1967.
[2] See Chapters VIII and IX.

1

in babies below two years of age, but which become of increasing importance as the children grow out of infancy into early childhood.[1]

A wider profile is therefore now possible covering virtually the whole range of abilities among children of the pre-school and infant school populations and catering also for those children who are too handicapped to be found in schools, but are seen in hospitals and clinics. As in the earlier tests, "equality of difficulty" in the separate sub-scales has been regarded as of primary importance, as it is upon the validity of this principle that mental diagnosis of this kind rests. In the present sequences this "equality of difficulty" *at each age level*, has been finally achieved, thus providing for the possibility of what we have called "differential diagnosis of mental status" throughout these important early years.

As will be shown in later chapters, large and representative samples of children of the required ages, have been included in the research, having been found and tested in many parts of the country. The total sample therefore on which the necessary standardisation work has been carried out contains 2,260 complete test results, and many other tests were taken covering certain parts of the range.

In planning the Scales the policy throughout this investigation has been to go to the children themselves for answers to our questions concerning their abilities. Thus we have kept the tests as close as possible to the normal interests, activities and general mental development of young children.

As a psychologist with more than forty years' experience of mental tests, and mental testing, the author is naturally familiar with many other tests, and some items in these new scales will inevitably resemble tests in other scales, but no items have been deliberately included from other scales, and all have been selected or devised on the basis of the responses of the children tested in this research. The majority of the 468 test items of these Scales are original to this book, and many have been adapted from the everyday experience of children's activities, and the continuous day by day observation of children everywhere.

The author undoubtedly owes a good deal to the work of Professor Arnold Gesell, whose extensive writings about babies and young children provide a perennial source of inspiration; and like all who work in the field of Mental Testing the author is grateful also for the work of Professor L. M. Terman, and Professor Maud Merrill, for

---

[1] For further discussion of this Scale see Chapter VI, p. 39 *et seq.*

their revisions of the Binet-Simon tests, which we have also used for correlation purposes.

In Part I of this book we shall present the methods used in the collection of the data for this study, also the design and building of the six scales that make up the complete examination.

In Part II we shall describe the organization of the data, the classifying of the items, the recording of the results, and the standardisation of the six separate scales. Here also the statistical findings will be presented. Two Chapters then follow describing the profiles of both normal and handicapped children.

In Part III the details of each of the six scales of the test, will be separately described, together with the method of administering each test item, and the necessary scoring standards.

PART I

CONSTRUCTING THE NEW SCALES

CHAPTER II

CONSTRUCTING THE TESTS FOR THE EXTENSION OF THE SCALES

Some preliminary considerations.

Observation of children.

ONE cannot stress too often the significance of careful and detailed observation of children if we are to understand them, perceive their thoughts, or interpret their behaviour. Still more important does this become for the investigator who is engaged in building a Scale of Tests. There is, in fact, scarcely any limit in this field of work, to what can be learned by the observation of children, at play, at home, on the street, in trains or buses, and in their own homes and gardens.

The *voice* of a child on a bus a few seats away, exclaiming at what he sees passing along a busy street, or raised in questioning words to a companion, gives the eavesdropper information about the child and some idea of his age, passing interests, demeanor etc. The very inflection of the raised voice can betray a child's approximate age, for the voices of babies under two years old, differ markedly from those of children three or four years of age; and voices continue to change as children grow older. Indeed, do they not change for us all throughout life?

The subject matter of a child's happy *speech* is also significant, being indicative of his interests. The quality of his vocabulary, the length of sentences used, the accuracy of pronunciation, the type of error made, all these are significant. The child's struggle for verbal expression is interesting and also quite delightful to observe, and to record.

In a similar way the *physical movements* of little children attract the attention. It is not always realized that tremendous mental effort on the part of the child goes into mastering the locomotor series itself. The clumsy balance of the very young child gives place to the gradual acquisition of poise and finally of grace of movement largely through the child's own effort. The development of *manual skills*, such as the gradual acquisition of the power to hold, grasp, and

7

manipulate objects in the environment, have a close relationship to items in test sequences such as, using a pencil on paper, holding and throwing a ball, building with bricks, threading beads, or turning a skipping rope. Observation of casual incidents, combine to give a first general impression of the age or ability level of a child, as he tries to grasp the meaning and significance of so many things in his complex environment.

The problem of the psychologist is how to classify, or make use of, such observations when building a new Scale of Tests. It has sometimes been fashionable for those wishing to build a new scale of tests, to gather items, individually selected from other tests to build a new scale. This practice is pernicious, and cannot take the place of genuine first hand observation. Moreover, each individual item of any scale, must be standardised *in its new situation*, in relation to the new sequence of which it then forms a part. It is of importance to stress in this connection that individual items in a sequence seldom carry the same mental-age increment, or ascend in equi-distant steps from one age level to another. These values are of course measured by the percentages of children passing each item, at each age level, and the items are then placed in strict order of difficulty on a percentage basis. Nonetheless it is the *total* sequence of items in a scale that is significant, and each item carries for the investigator, a known value in that sequence. Therefore, a haphazard selection of items from other scales, that may appeal to the builder of a new scale, cannot possibly in itself produce an accurate or satisfactory result, without much further testing and standardisation.

Each and every item used in the present scales had been selected and individually and separately standardised on adequate samples of tests from normal children, before it was felt that a reliable scale had emerged for use in this important work of differential diagnosis.

Further to this as will be seen in the following chapters, it is the problem of "equality of difficulty" between the six major sequences, *at each age level*, and throughout the eight years of the Scales, that must be solved, if we can, at the end, say categorically that a particular child is failing, or succeeding, in any specific direction, or doing better in one of the major categories than in another. This is the *raison d'etre*, the basic condition that provides for the significance of the profile in diagnosis, although each sequence measures a different aspect of learning, or mental growth, the scales must all be equal in difficulty and statistically similar throughout.

After the earlier tests on the first two years had been in use for some time, as already explained, it was realised that we could not stop at that point, that is at two years of mental age; but the tests must be carried further for the sake of those somewhat older children who might benefit from the profile type of assessment.

On the one hand the cleverest of babies tested between 18 and 24 months of age, frequently showed that they would be able to go further, and might pass items of the third year or beyond, if such were provided in all the sub-scales. We improvised in this situation as a temporary measure, by using items from the third year of other scales, and adding the extra mental age credits thus earned to the total examination result.[1] For reasons just expressed this was unsatisfactory, and in such cases also, because of classification problems the characteristic profile could not be maintained.

Conversely certain retarded children doing other tests that began with the third year, needed test items for below that level to complete their assessment at the *lower* end, and provide the necessary basic part of the examination. For the same reason to use the first two years of the new scales for this purpose could also only be a temporary expedient.

There was no escape! It was soon realised that *all* the separate scales, each measuring a different avenue of development, that together constitute the examination, and produce the profile, must be extended beyond the end of the second year, to be adequate and effective.

The next problem was to decide exactly how far to carry them. After much consideration and much testing of children between two and five years of age and beyond, it was decided to go high enough to make this new method available to the end of the Infant School period. Actually in their final form these tests are adequate for the testing of *mentally handicapped* children far *beyond* the eighth year, where the retardation requires it.

This was altogether a tremendous task for one psychologist to contemplate, and even with some generous help, as time went on, with the gathering of the data in schools, the whole project occupied several further years, before the testing was all completed, on adequate representative numbers of children, of the required ages. Then followed the completion of the quite extensive desk work, the organising of the data, card indexing, and the standardisation, and much other statistical work also followed.

Moreover the reader will already have realised that the work of

[1] See "The Abilities of Babies", p. 218.

extending these scales was a project that from the beginning, was by no means accomplished entirely at the desk, or in the play-room or consulting room. It meant coming into contact individually with large numbers of normal children of the required ages, not only formally in the test situation, but also informally wherever one went.

Personal observation, is of course paramount; children in shops, in parks, in trains, and in one's professional work, all provide preliminary data and suggestions for this type of work. A few examples might be relevant.

One is proceeding along a street near one's home. Across the way three small boys are observed with tricycles, riding or trying to ride, up a slight gradient on the opposite footpath. The observer slackens her pace and walks on slowly. The oldest child gets on his new and beautiful machine, places his hands and feet with confidence, and rides away ahead of the others. The next child finds the gradient awkward, his feet tend to slip from the pedals, but he perseveres and soon he is laboriously in pursuit of his companion up the path. The third little one on a tiny machine struggles valiantly, wobbles across the path, loses his foothold and is in danger of collapsing into the gutter. At this point the observer crosses swiftly to his rescue. He smiles cheerfully, saying "I can, I can". The confident little chap is set on his way, but not before his age is ascertained. "I'm nearly fwee", he announces. Proceeding along the road the other two boys are presently met with. A friendly chat follows. They tell their ages too.

It is of importance to make careful notes of information however informally gleaned. It all adds to one's total experience and impression of children. As soon as the boys are out of sight a note book from the handbag and a pencil are produced, and the ages of those three tricycle riders, and their respective achievements provide a little more 'grist to the mill'. Also the memory of those three with their new tricycles, and the pleasure the incident gave, becomes a permanent possession. The experience also provided the beginning of another short testing sequence for the Locomotor Scale!

Similarly there was a short and very happy session with a group of little girls encountered skipping and trying to skip, with ropes, in a cul-de-sac, not far from Great Ormond Street Hospital for Sick Children. The adult "helped" by holding one end of the rope and watched the tiny girls jump over, and then later try to skip. They laughed and chatted with the adult who asked them when their birthdays were, and who also noted mentally the level of their speech, and made a few other observations. Quite a lot was learned in a few minutes and later in the "Undergound" on the way home a few useful notes of that brief encounter were made, and another sequence had been born.

Children's speech is around us all the time, as we go about in our neighbourhood, wherever it may be, for children are everywhere. Everywhere also there is this raw material of child psychology. The best advice that can be given to any student "taking up" child study, is in the first instance, thus informally and unobtrusively, to observe and again observe, but always to chrystallise and make permanent and as accurate as possible, these observations, by making *notes* of what is observed.

The speech of little children is delightful and instructive and valuable work can also be done by systematic recordings at regular intervals, of the speech of one or more children.

Observation of children, as we have said provides the raw material of child psychology, this is true also of medicine, child psychiatry, psychotherapy, of pedagogy, social work, nursing, and in fact of every profession that is concerned with the well being of children. It is basic to test construction.

Such observation as has been described in this chapter may appear haphazard and incomplete. This is because such observations need to be multiplied many times, and collected under controlled conditions. The observations must also be recorded, related with great accuracy to the ages of the children observed, before they can be used as even the raw data of new mental tests. The more precise and systematic observations that finally enabled these scales to be built up, standardised and made available to other workers, will be described in the following chapters.

CHAPTER III

BUILDING THE EXTENDED SCALES
COLLECTING THE DATA

AFTER much observational work, both formal and incidental, among children between two and eight years of age had been carried out, a stage was reached when provisional lists of test items, likely to be suitable in the Extended Scales could be prepared. These would, for the most part, carry the five sub-scales of the first two years, already in existence, on to the years of early childhood, which in the final version were successfully carried to the end of the eighth year and into the ninth.

These earlier sub-scales previously standardised on tests from 604 babies between 0 and 24 months of age were:[1]

Scale A.   The Locomotor Scale.

Scale B.   The Personal-Social Scale.

Scale C.   Hearing and Speech Development.

Scale D.   Hand and Eye Co-ordination.

Scale E.   A Scale of Performance Tests.

These Scales were gradually extended by adding to each in a provisional way, items suited to slightly older children, in each of the five categories. These were new items likely to be useful, or items already used on a number of children, in the preliminary testing already mentioned or were more advanced items of the same tests. For example, **Scale A,** the Locomotor Scale, acquired such tests as "jumping off steps", in a short sequence of increasing difficulty; walking tip-toe, running, hopping, jumping over a rope, skipping etc., and in the course of testing and observational work in school playgrounds and elsewhere, other items of a locomotor type were introduced. All these additions were made on a temporary and purely experimental basis. Some items thus included were later discarded, as being too difficult to administer, or were found statistically unreliable or otherwise unsuitable.

Scale B was extended sometimes as the result of enquiring of the

---

[1] See "The Abilities of Babies", University of London Press, 1954, 1964, 1967.

parents concerning the child's helpfulness in the home, or in learning to wash and dress himself, or manage neatly at table, etc. This last matter was often studied when visiting infant and nursery schools by observing the children having their school lunch, and then quietly asking their ages, and unobtrusively making notes. All such items were introduced on a *provisional* basis and retention in the scale depended on the standardisation.

Scale C grew quickly, for children are usually willing to talk freely, either to the adult or to one another, and many items of the speech series *began* as the result of conversations with children in the playgrounds or elsewhere. Also the test materials being very attractive to the children gave rise to much incidental conversation during tests, and as much as possible of the speech of the children during the testing *was taken down*. Pictures shown to the children during the tests, also helped to stimulate verbal expression, and the responses to these were also *fully recorded*.

Scales D and E involved the introduction of some new test material, based for Scale E on the form boards and brick-boxes, originally designed by the author for the first two years of the scales, but now modified and added to, in order to introduce some more difficult items for the standardisation of the Extended Scales.

Other manipulative tasks also were included in Scale D, and drawing tests formed a large part of this "Hand and Eye Scale".

Thus all this building of the scales and gradual gathering of the data, was carried out on a provisional basis. Later on, lists of items were duplicated for each series, for use in further testing, including Scale F, a new scale to be described below.

In this provisional testing, individual items could be scored plus or minus, but no M.A.s or scores, or quotients could at this stage be worked out. Nonetheless this material and the accompanying information as it increased, gradually became the basic data on which the *final* tests were built, and the standardisation carried out.

The aim was to represent in the tests the entire range of abilities for the ages in question, or to include as far as possible all aspects of learning and mental growth, in a wide profile. There were however two directions concerning which major decisions had to be made, and which involved considerable further work.

Scale F. I. It was early realised that there were certain skills and items of learning, that could not be fitted logically into these five scales when extended, and that a sixth scale would need to be added for children above two years of age, thus providing a six-stem profile for the older children. This new scale, Scale F, we called *Practical Reasoning*. It included such items as simple arithmetical tasks, counting, repetition of digits, comparing objects for size, length, height, weight etc. Even the simplest of these items were in the vast majority of cases, too difficult for babies under two years of age; they belong essentially to the period of early childhood rather than to that of infancy. The effects of this inclusion of a sixth stem to the profile, for the older children, on the scoring and general plan of the entire scale will be dealt with later.

II. The other major change concerns the *first two years of the scales* which now become, in this connection, not only a separate and complete scale for testing babies under two years of age, but also the basic period of tests for the extension of the scales into the early childhood period. This further change will be more fully described when we deal with the whole question of the standardisation in Chapter VI; but the earlier scales still remain the most useful scales for testing little babies under about eighteen months of age.

In due course permission was obtained from certain local authorities for testing of this kind to be done by the author in infant schools, nursery schools, play centres, and elsewhere in London, within easy reach of the centre. In this connection I shall always be grateful to Dr. J. A. Scott, Medical Officer of Health, and members of his staff, for their kind co-operation. Many children also were brought by the parents to the Child Development Research Centre for a test to be done. Parents were frequently present during the actual testing at the Centre, and some of these parents showed great interest in the work. They appreciated any advice or help that could be given on the basis of a test result. They also told their friends about our work, who in their turn sometimes brought other children for testing.

Thus the provisional data grew, but numbers of tests were accumulated somewhat slowly, and much other work was also going on at the Centre. The lists of items were kept under constant review as tests were added and as soon as a quantity of data was available for study, improvements could be made. All test results were systematically recorded, item by item, on the large "charts" referred to earlier,[1] in readiness for the standardisation work to commence.

In 1960 several psychologists and medical officers already familiar with the earlier scales, volunteered to help with the extension testing. By this time some 400 children over two years of age had already been tested by the author at the Centre and elsewhere in the London

[1] See "The Abilities of Babies", p. 48, and elsewhere.

area, and the samples below two years had also been increased. Following an invitation from the Glasgow Corporation in 1961 for a course on this approach to mental testing to be held in that city, a team of six people, four psychologists and two medical officers, all already familiar with the earlier scales, offered to help with the gathering of the data. The author herself went to Glasgow and enjoyed a very interesting and stimulating week of meetings. There, very pleasant arrangements were made at the Central Child Guidance Clinic for the demonstration testing, and the six volunteers were introduced to the Extension Scales in their provisional form; a number of children were tested and lectures given, and many new friends were made.

After this visit regular parcels of completed tests arrived in London from the Glasgow team, who were kept supplied from London with the necessary apparatus, and the duplicated lists of items. These lists were fastened together to form temporary record books, one for each child tested, with pages for the necessary social data and other background information, also, with ample foolscap provision for the comments of the examiner, recordings of the actual verbal responses of the children, and for their drawings, writing, etc.

Following on this encouraging development, with its promise of Scottish samples, other psychologists and medical officers, who were already familiar with the first two years of the scales, and who were working in other parts of England and Wales, on hearing of this adventure also offered their services. These officers visited the Centre in London in twos and threes, for a few days to obtain instruction at the research stage, and see some testing done. Apparatus and a supply of the provisional record books were made available to them.

Others in England and Wales joined the team, and the author herself visited Wales, and counties in England to test children of the mining communities. Others of the team tested children in Swansea and Cardiff. Later with the kind co-operation of the authorities, we tested children in Wiltshire where one of the team was working as psychologist for the Wiltshire Education Authority and in Somerset visited rural villages in the farming areas, testing children in the schools and sometimes in the homes of the children. A good sample too were tested in sea-side resorts on the coast of Somerset. Many pleasant memories remain of the kindness of the medical officers, teachers, and those of the parents one met, and the general enthusiam was helpful and encouraging. It was also pleasant for the writer to return to areas where she had lived and worked earlier in her life.

These visits and the work of the team in many parts of the country added very valuable data to the research. The quantities of information collected in the provisional record books, grew in a satisfactory way. All the people who took part in the gathering of the data, twelve in number, worked voluntarily with permission of their authorities, by testing children of the required ages and paternal occupation groups, as they found convenient in the course of their work in schools, clinics and welfare centres.

One psychologist, on her retirement from full-time work, immediately offered to help with the testing, and worked for a lengthy period in schools in Surrey. Some of these friends were able to do a lot of testing, others could do only a few tests, but all did what they could to help our project, whilst usually engaged full time in other work. The author made many brief visits to places away from London to test children of special groups, some in residential care.

Meanwhile the testing continued at the Child Development Research Centre, in between the author's visits to other parts of the country. It was felt important to test children in as many different environments as could be arranged for, to keep the samples as representative as possible of the whole country in each year of life, and every opportunity that arose was accepted. Nonetheless there was work to be done in London. Children were awaiting appointments for tests or re-tests at the Centre, and here of course the data was accumulating throughout these several years. Lecture courses on Child Development and Mental Testing were also held from time to time at the Centre.

Several hundred tests had been carried out by the whole team, when it was at last decided that sufficient data was available for the standardisation of the tests to begin. The bulk of the work of the whole project naturally fell to the originator to carry.

When we came to the big task of sorting, card indexing and filing the material, valuable help was at hand from the one indefatigable secretary, who had 'held the fort', kept the duplicating going of the provisional record books, and the correspondence with the team, during the several years occupied by the gathering of the data. In studying the bulk of the information available, in the provisional record books, and in the earlier tests of babies, and including results from normal children seen at the Centre for demonstrations during lecture courses, and all those that had been seen in so many places by us all, some 3,000 children had been given these Scales over the years. A considerable proportion of the older children had also been given Terman Merrill Tests. Many tests taken at early stages of the work, before all the new test items had been incorporated, could not be used in the final standardisation, as they were too incomplete. Special cases were in general not included. Nonetheless the information provided by these earlier, or otherwise incomplete tests, had all helped us to build the six scales. These Scales went through several revisions before the completed samples of 2,260 tests could be used for the standardisation of the final version.

In the next chapter we shall consider more fully these samples, and show their representative nature from several points of view, including a study of paternal occupation groups, and shall show how our total sample compares with the Official Classification of Occupation Groups in the 1951 census.

In Chapters VI to VIII we shall present the results of the standardisation.

CHAPTER IV

THE TOTAL SAMPLE
ITS REPRESENTATIVE NATURE

IN undertaking a research of the kind under discussion in this book, it was felt to be imperative, not only to build up an adequate series of test items for the Measurement of the Abilities of Young Children, but to see that the samples of the child population on whose test results the standardisation was to be carried out, were as representative as possible of the total community.

To gather a representative sample of a population is no easy matter and in these islands considerable variations exist in regard to the environments of the children that might have a bearing on test results. Some children live in crowded town areas surrounded by people, by buildings, by traffic, and are taught in crowded classrooms; others live in considerable isolation in country and coastal areas.

A perfect sample is of course not "a sample" at all, for only a *total* population of a defined area, can be regarded as a perfect or complete sample from the statistical point of view. But of course to take one place only, and study a cross section of a child population thoroughly within a geographical region, has been recommended, and indeed carried out in at least one extensive research, in which the present writer played some part.[1] But when all is laborously fulfilled the result may be a sample of great interest, but one which does not, of course, necessarily represent the *total* community, of which the defined area forms a part. As it would not be practical to apply scales of tests to the total child population of Great Britain, however valuable that might be, the next best policy would seem to be to use certain criteria, such as the occupations of the fathers, for a suitable comparison with the total population. The reason for this is, of course, that this information has been collected at each periodic census of the population, and if our samples although so much smaller, are comparable statistically, this should reassure us that at

[1] See "Studies of a Child Population". Nos. I to IV Roberts, Norman and Griffiths. Bibliography, p. 175.

least each section of the working community has been satisfactorily represented.

In the present study the examiners at first tested any children of the relevant ages, as they were met with in the various schools and institutions visited, or were seen elsewhere. In so doing they also collected in the prepared provisional record books certain items of information about each child that were of social importance; the date of birth of the child, his position in his family, his sex, etc., and the occupation of the child's father. These matters were routinely entered whenever a child was tested.

As soon however as a reasonable quantity of background information as well as records of the responses of the children to the tests, had been accumulated, it became important to discover, and systematically record, the proportion of the children tested who belonged to each of the main paternal occupation groups. The purpose of this recording of occupations was to keep us at the Centre duly informed of the representative nature of the samples as they were collected. As the results came to hand this information was transferred to a special record (or chart) where we could study at a glance how the groups were expanding in each year and month. We could then act accordingly in advising our friends who were helping with the testing what children to look for in the schools and elsewhere. Nonetheless we did sometimes receive a test that could not be used because we already had sufficient of certain groups. These unwanted tests were however very few, and even these contributed, in some measure, to the total mass of information.

When the study of this problem of representative samples was first undertaken by us in connection with the earlier standardisation of the first two years of the tests, early in 1950, there had been no previous census taken in Great Britain since 1931 owing to the intervening war years. The writer resorted therefore at that time to the use of the most recent census available, and to a Study of Occupation Groups carried out by Dr. Florence Goodenough, for a similar purpose to our own, in the United States. This question was fully discussed and the results presented in "The Abilities of Babies", 1964, pp. 56, 57.

When a few years later we began to test these older children and also to add to our earlier samples of babies, it became important to have more recent information concerning the Paternal Occupation Groups of this country, at the time that the bulk of the testing was done. Information from the 1961 census was not yet available, and some of the relevant information is still not available at the time of writing. We were therefore advised to use the 1951 British Census findings on this question. This year (1951) was also nearer to the time when the main part of the testing of little babies had been done, and also corresponded within a year or two with the dates of birth of most of the children tested later.

As is well known it has been customary in official documents since about 1911 to arrange the large number of Unit Groups in the "Classification of Occupations" into a number of broad categories or classes, as an aid to statistical work of certain kinds. These main categories are five in number and provide a broad classification that would appear to be adequate to the purposes of the present investigation.

These five Classes are:

Class I.   Professional etc., Occupations.
Class II.   Intermediate Occupations.
Class III.   Skilled Occupations.
Class IV.   Partly-skilled Occupations.
Class V.   Unskilled Occupations.

We shall now therefore show the relationship of our own total samples of children when the occupations of their fathers are compared with the 1951 census figures of Paternal Occupation. These are shown below.

It will be seen from Table I that the relationship between the percentages of our children in the five main paternal occupation groups is closely comparable with the census figures. We can therefore conclude that from this point of view we have indeed in this study a good and representative sample of the total population of Great Britain, in spite of the somewhat haphazard way in which it was collected.

TABLE I

PATERNAL OCCUPATION

(Comparison with the 1951 British Census)

Class	Actual number of children tested	% of 2,260	% in 1951 British Census
I	75	3.3	3.3
II	330	14.6	14.5
III	1,206	53.4	52.9
IV	355	15.7	16.1
V	294	13.0	13.1

It may be of interest also to show *in greater detail* the close relationship by "Paternal Occupation Groups" of the samples of children included in the standardisation of the Scales, with the figures for the whole country; for this would appear to be a matter of considerable importance, should the new tests be used in broader population studies, or in other kinds of research or clinical work. Below will therefore be found a more detailed analysis of these figures by *age groups* of the children. This will illustrate the fact that in each year of life we aimed at and largely achieved representative samples by occupation groups.

TABLE II

PATERNAL OCCUPATION GROUPS

A Further Analysis by Age Groups of the figures in Table I

National	%	3.3	14.5	52.9	16.1	13.1
Year (ages)	N	Group I	Group II	Group III	Group IV	Group V
I	427	3.28	14.75	53.86	15.00	13.11
II	436	3.44	14.91	52.75	15.83	13.07
III	327	3.36	14.98	53.51	15.56	12.54
IV	274	3.28	14.59	53.65	15.69	12.77
V	285	3.16	15.09	53.68	15.09	12.98
VI	223	3.58	13.90	51.57	17.04	13.90
VII	211	3.31	14.69	53.08	16.13	12.79
VIII	77	2.60	10.40	57.14	16.88	12.98
Total......	2,260					

Note: Year VIII is a small sample of children, N=77.
Total number of children tested N=2,260.

As already mentioned every effort was made to get children included in the samples from different parts of the country. In Table III below we now therefore present the details of the geographical distribution of the children tested.

TABLE III

GEOGRAPHICAL AREAS
WHERE THE CHILDREN WERE FOUND AND TESTED

Year of Age	England	Wales	Scotland	Total
I	400	10	17	427
II	300	58	78	436
III	174	99	54	327
IV	169	50	55	274
V	158	55	72	285
VI	119	18	86	223
VII	157	8	46	211
VIII	44	9	24	77
Totals	1,521	307	432	2,260

As well as searching for our samples in different parts of the country, we also looked for children in schools and in other institutions, that is, in nursery schools, day nurseries, infant welfare centres, child guidance clinics, and some were seen in residential care; and a large number came to the Child Development Research Centre, or were seen in play centres or nurseries and schools in North London. In Table IV this information is summarised.

TABLE IV

Year of Age	Infant Welfare and Health Centres	Day Nurseries	Child Development Research Centre	Seen Privately	Tested in Hospitals	Residential Care	Nursery Schools	Play Centres	Child Guidance Clinics	Day Schools	Totals
I	218	96	59	28	21	5	0	0	0	0	427
II	232	132	28	12	24	8	0	0	0	0	436
III	107	101	58	14	3	7	19	7	11	0	327
IV	56	67	61	13	10	11	33	17	6	0	274
V	66	47	67	10	0	5	51	15	11	13	285
VI	17	15	42	4	7	7	6	0	5	120	223
VII	8	0	31	0	7	4	0	2	0	159	211
VIII	16	0	4	0	5	1	0	0	0	51	77
Totals	720	458	350	81	77	48	109	41	33	343	2,260

Institutions etc., where the Children were found and tested

The question is sometimes asked as to how many boys and how many girls we had in our samples. Naturally as we were dealing throughout with babies and children of the younger ages, it was not necessary to visit separate institutions to find boys or girls and try in any way to obtain similar numbers of each sex. Our method was to test children of the particular age group that we needed at the time, and to record the basic information, mainly in order to get our samples as accurate as possible from the point of view of parental occupation groups, as already explained. In this way the children were listed from the registers, if we were working in schools, and from the children in attendance when we visited other places. Actually we found that rather more boys than girls were tested, and this happened frequently with both babies and little children under school age. The final totals of children included in the research also showed this tendency. On enquiry of the Home Office we were informed that during the years when we were gathering the data, rather more boys than girls were born in this country. Here are the figures for the boys and girls in the total sample:

TABLE V

	Boys	Girls	Totals
Year I	214	213	427
Year II	245	191	436
Year III	166	161	327
Year IV	138	136	274
Year V	134	151	285
Year VI	113	110	223
Year VII	114	97	211
Year VIII	38	39	77
Totals	1,162	1,098	2,260

During the testing and gathering of the data several opportunities arose for the testing of twins, as these were found in the schools and elsewhere. Multiple births are always of interest in psychological work. We did not specially search for these, but actually met pairs of twins in the samples, or we were asked by the teachers to test them. Normal twins tested were included in our work, we found and included 32 pairs of twins, and 2 sets of quads. The first set of quads was included in the earlier work as reported in "The Abilities of Babies" in 1954. The second set was tested more recently in Glasgow. We did not meet any triplets or other multiple births during the research.

PART II

STANDARDISATION OF THE SCALE AND DIAGNOSTIC IMPLICATIONS

CHAPTER V

STANDARDISING THE SCALE

In the previous chapters we have described something of the way in which these tests were constructed, and the way the testing of larger numbers of children was established, and carried out by the author, assisted generously by a team of psychologists and medical officers, who helped to collect the raw data of the tests, in various parts of the country.

At the Centre, faced with a growing volume of information, and these provisional test results, it was necessary that careful and accurate records should be built up, as the data grew, and that all this information should be easily accessible. The large sheets of squared paper already referred to, were used throughout, to record the individual test results, item by item, after all the provisional record forms had been scored. This was to provide a complete and permanent record also, of the way the standardisation work was carried out. These we refer to as our "charts".[1] There are now several hundred of these, filed for constant reference and for future research, in the large drawers of a plan chest.

Organising the data

As the results recorded by the examiners in the provisional record books, came to hand, the individual details of each child's successes and failures were recorded on these charts. We use the $\frac{1}{4}$ inch squared paper (size 24" by 18"). One sheet of this paper can accommodate as as many as 80 results (or more if needed) from *one* sub-scale of the tests. It was thus possible to enter the results for each two-months age group on one such sheet or chart. Beginning with the first two months of the first year, and continuing to the 96th month, that it to the end of the 8th year, the material for *one* sub-scale, (for example, Scale A, the Locomotor Scale), occupied 48 of these sheets or charts. Similarly records were built up for each of the other sub-scales, Sacle B. Personal-Social Scale; Scale C. Hearing and Speech; Scale D. Hand and Eye Co-ordination and Scale E. Performance

---

[1] See "The Abilities of Babies", p. 48.

Tests, each occupying 48 further charts. Finally Scale F. Practical Reasoning, which, beginning with months 21 and 22, occupied 38 further sheets. Thus 278 of these charts were built up to accommodate all the responses of the 2,260 children, included in the research.

On each chart the names of the children were entered at the top of the columns, and the chronological ages in *months* in the square immediately below. The items of the particular sub-scale were listed and numbered down the left-hand side of the chart. Spaces were left for the inevitable changes that would arise from the standardisation. In practice the two-months group has proved convenient throughout this work.

Each item passed or failed by a child was recorded by the symbol — or √ in the appropriate ¼ inch square. The number of children passing each item was counted *across* the page and entered in a column on the right-hand side, ready to be converted into percentages and entered in a further column when the results were more complete. Thus material for a study of that particular two-months group came into being, ready to be transferred later to percentage tables when the data on adjacent charts was more complete.

Meanwhile by counting down the page perpendicularly these same plus and minus symbols, the *scores* for each individual child were recorded at the *foot* of each column. Later these raw scores were converted into mental ages, then divided by the chronological ages already referred to, to provide the quotients for that particular section of one scale, and recorded in the same columns below the mental ages. This was the procedure used on all the 278 charts. All the relevant data for each two-month group was thus recorded and made available for the next stage in the work, and also remains as a permanent record of this part of the standardisation.

Quotients were arrived at like intelligence quotients in other scales (M.A. × 100 over C.A.) = I.Q.

As we had six scales we named the quotients as follows:

QA = Locomotor Quotient.
QB = Personal-Social Quotient.
QC = Verbal Quotient (Hearing and Speech Scale).
QD = Hand and Eye Quotient.
QE = Performance Quotient, and
QF = Practical Quotient, for Scale F, known as Practical Reasoning.

The G.Q. or General Intelligence Quotient is arrived at by taking the average of the quotients of the six sub-scales of a child's total performance.

After a considerable amount of information had thus been recorded on the charts, the next matters for consideration involved decisions about the number of items to be retained throughout the scales, for no final quotients could be arrived at until all the scales were complete and had reached their final form. We had therefore to decide how many items to include in each scale, and in each year of each scale, and which items if any to omit. For these problems of course the percentage tables provided most of the answers. These were our next concern, for again if we were to achieve equality of difficulty in all the scales, it would be convenient also to have the same number of items not only in each year of any one scale, but in all of them across the six scales.

In planning the scales it was realised that the individual test items for the older children, would inevitably take longer to administer, than the numerous more quickly given items for the little babies. Problems of scoring and allotting mental age credits had to be considered, and the most suitable number of items for each major sequence for each year of the tests, both above and below two years, had to be decided. In fact the method of combining the tests of the earlier scales with the later ones, and adapting them as the basic part of the new scales, so as to provide ease of scoring throughout the entire range of the tests, became important.

The scoring in *weeks* of mental age credit, so far used for the babies,[1] would have to give place to scoring in months throughout, as in other scales for older children, and so bring the *scoring* of the first two years of the earlier part of the scales into line with this. For example it would have been too cumbersome to continue to have three items per week in the first year, two items per week in the second year, as previously, and then change at the end of the second year to credits in months! The final decision was therefore to arrange, for two items per month in each sub-scale, from 0 to 24 months, thus each item would carry the value of a half-month of credit. There were thus to be 24 items in the first year, and 24 in the second year, making 48 in *each* sub-scale for the entire two years of the baby Scales. Multiplying this figure by five, because there are five scales in the first two years, thus provides 240 test items for this early part of the Scales, or 10 items for each month. Thus the scoring of this part of the Scales is vastly simplified, as for example, a baby scoring

---

[1] See "The Abilities of Babies".

a total of 135 items, all in the first two years, would have a mental age of 13.5 months. To insert the decimal point in the total score, thus dividing it by ten, would be all that was necessary for a quick result, were that required. See Summary of Test Results, page 170.

Nonetheless the new scales being described in this book are not intended to supersede the scales as described in "The Abilities of Babies", where *young* babies are being assessed. The 1954 scales are as useful and valid as ever. This has been proved to be so throughout the years in which many thousands of babies have been tested with them by the numerous professional workers who have taken up the testing of babies by this method. So that for those doctors and psychologists who test mainly very young babies, in researches and studies of early infancy or for the "At risk" or "Observation" register, or for investigation of special disabilities, such as deafness, cerebral palsy, mongolism, etc., the earlier version being fuller, especially in the first year, is still the best scale to use, giving, as it does, more opportunity for detailed observation.

It is important to note that with the above considerations in mind, the scoring of the first two years by the earlier tests, was of necessity somewhat time consuming, and some modification was necessary when the first two years of the tests became the basic part of the longer scale. This has led inevitably to some revision of these first two years of the scales, in fact to the omission of certain items of the first year, and some increase in the number of items in the second year. The result of this and also the increase in the size of the samples, led to a complete re-standardisation of the first two years of the Scale. The modification of this early part of the range was somewhat complicated.

1. The first principle of the standardisation of several parallel scales, namely, "equality of difficulty" between them had to be maintained.

2. The second consideration was neither to add nor to remove items, if to do so would impair the diagnostic usefulness of the test.

In eliminating a number of items from the first year, as many as seven in each scale, care was taken not to remove any particular item, if to do so would eliminate an important diagnostic observation. This meant that any item that stood alone, and was not one of a definite short sequence, had to remain. Where there *was* a short sequence of items however, one, but only one could be discarded. The problem as to which one to discard, then depended on the statistical position.

The desired result was gradually achieved.

In the second year a few additional items were needed there being 21 in each scale where 24 was the required number. It was not possible to introduce any quite new items, without much further testing. It was however found possible to allot "double" credits to several items, and also to divide certain items into two stages, or make a new item, representing a new stage, in a short sequence, where a numerical value was involved, and where the evidence in the existing test results was sufficient to justify this. For example, item C II 8, "Uses five clear words" made a new item, where previously 4 or 5 clear words was the standard. This one decision involved searching into the provisional record forms, and earlier records, and then adding one additional point where babies had known five words. A similar process was necessary for certain other items. With the added evidence of larger samples at the end of the second year, it was for example, possible to include "Picture vocabulary –4" as another item. Each possibility had to be thoroughly investigated, and its effect on the "equality of difficulty" in the sub-scales scrutinised before the change could be made.

A further set of circumstances also contributed to the problem and made the restandardisation more valuable. Naturally, over the years, a good many babies both normal and handicapped had been tested at the Child Development Research Centre, sometimes as demonstration cases during lecture courses, and also tests of children in the first two years were occasionally contributed by members of the research team, or tests taken earlier were sent to us for re-test purposes, children in the new research having been tested previously when under two years of age. This meant that the number of babies in the new standardisation could be increased from 604 to 863.

The number of items in the extended part of the scales had also to be decided. For this we relied on the percentage tables, selecting the items and placing them in correct order of difficulty, limiting the numbers in each scale to 6 items in each year, from the third to the eighth year of the tests, thus giving in each scale two months credit for each item.

Gradually the scales emerged and took on their final form, each item being placed as near as possible to the point at which 50% of the children had passed it.

Later, mental ages could be arrived at, and quotients worked out for each child in each age group, on the charts where all this work was done The proof of the accuracy of all this standardisation work lay in the final quotients. Wherever in the course of the work, in any section, the result was found to be less satisfactory, the average quotient being too high or too low to be acceptable, modifications had to be carried out, perhaps by eliminating an item with all the repercussions that would have on adjacent sections, or sometimes combining items, or dividing one into two, and so on.

In Table VI will be found the quotients, showing those arrived at for each of the six scales, and the total G.Q's. The total quotient for the whole sample of 2,260 children is **100.18.**

Quite early in the work it became necessary to card index the material. Cards were made to take the results for each child, and a further index was prepared for the background and social information in each case. Thus two indexes were prepared. One index contains the final results of the six scales, also ages, mental ages and quotients, tabulated on each card for statistical work, and this we called the "working index". The other index contains information about the test itself, where and when it was carried out. Also were here recorded the child's personal particulars, the number of tests taken, the name of the examiner, and other details. Everything was kept brief and uniform, and symbols were used, so that card sorting would be facilitated.

Several further years elapsed before it was felt that enough data had been collected to enable the records to be closed, the standardisation finalised, and the testing of further children for this research could cease, though certain children in the records were seen for re-tests, and follow-up studies, and for other purposes.

The standardisation of six separate but inter-related Scales, has been a lengthy and time consuming task. A great deal more could be done and we hope will be done, to extract further information from the records. The main objective has been to get each scale standardised as a separate and complete scale *valid in itself*, showing suitable averages and standard deviations. The second objective was to obtain "equality of difficulty" so far as possible between all the six scales *at every age level*, so that the main thesis of "differential diagnosis of mental status" could be maintained throughout. We shall show what degree of success has been achieved in this double task in the following chapters.

TABLE VI

TABLE OF QUOTIENTS IN EACH SUB-SCALE
ANNUAL GROUPINGS

Year	N.	A.Q.	B.Q.	C.Q.	D.Q.	E.Q.	F.Q.	G.Q.
I	427	99.78	99.76	100.19	99.60	99.42	—	99.78
II	436	100.35	100.12	98.85	100.73	99.90	—	99.81
III	327	100.83	100.52	100.13	99.91	98.86	99.58	100.39
IV	274	100.75	101.29	99.18	99.94	99.98	99.35	100.20
V	285	101.38	101.04	99.72	99.96	100.08	99.36	100.20
VI	223	100.74	100.37	100.87	102.32	101.44	100.60	101.43
VII	211	100.18	99.91	100.92	101.81	100.40	100.86	100.83
VIII	77	96.70	96.99	97.34	100.29	95.25	98.96	97.74
Total:	2260						Total G.Q.	100.18

CHAPTER VI

THE STANDARDISATION OF THE SEPARATE
SUB-SCALES AND THEIR SEVERAL FUNCTIONS

HAVING already given some idea of the children, who all unknowingly took part in this research, the range of their ages, the occupation groups of their parents, and the widely differing environments from whence they came, we must now turn our attention to the actual tests presented to them and the way in which these tests have been standardised to provide accurate and reliable test procedures. These scales may presently be used in population studies that might be undertaken, but will more frequently be used in diagnostic testing of both normal and handicapped children, wherever this can fulfil a useful purpose, e.g. in educational and clinical work.

As previously mentioned each sub-scale was devised to be a separate and complete scale in itself, each measuring only one avenue of learning or process of development, but measuring this one aspect as completely as possible.

Let us now therefore look at these six scales one by one and try to indicate the function that each series of tests performs, and how, when used together as a complete investigation, they can give an answer to, or throw significant light upon individual problems of development in infancy and early childhood. The individual result of a complete test on a child, can be shown graphically by means of the profile. Such a profile is arrived at for each child examined. The profile and its use as a diagnostic instrument will be described and demonstrated more fully in Chapters VIII and IX.

Each of the sub-scales measures a separate sequence of events, and if desired can be used for its own special function quite apart from the rest. We are therefore not dealing with one scale but with six separate scales, all equal in difficulty, but vastly different in content.

For example, studies of infant speech and language can be carried out by the use, in testing, of Scale C *alone*. Also the Locomotor Scale can be used to supplement observation in studies of physical activities and development in both normal and physically handicapped children. Or, two scales such as Scale A: 'Locomotor Development' and Scale D: 'Hand and Eye Co-ordination', might be used in conjunction with one another in an investigation into general physical efficiency in certain children. Scale C: 'Hearing and Speech' and Scale F: 'Practical Reasoning', might also be combined in studies of certain specific intellectual processes. In fact the Terman-Merrill Scale is largely a combination of test items of these two types.

Nonetheless, in spite of these possibilities, it is the *total* examination (the five-scale test for babies, or the six-scale test for older children from 2 to 8 years of age) that can give the complete developmental picture, and provide for a clear diagnostic indication for a handicapped child, and a valid profile. In fact the full test should always be applied as part of the preliminary investigation of the condition of a handicapped child, whatever the nature of the handicap may be.

Scale A: Locomotor Development

This scale though logically first in the test when assessing a child's capabilities, and important in relation to a possible health problem, should in general be taken *last*, when actually examining a child. It is placed first in the scales as it does provide a basis for objective observation and a first impression of the general maturity of a young child. Provisional scoring on the basis of such observation is frequently possible. At the same time from the testing angle, it is important to realise that any handling of the child by the examiner, if undertaken too soon in the course of the interview may produce resistance, weeping, emotional blocking, or shyness, or in a sturdier child, objection or refusal to respond.

In all this work with young children a gentle, quiet and slow approach is best. More serious from the testing point of view, is the situation where the child having been invited to run, jump, throw or kick a ball (and these are all test items), may decide that this is an occasion for boisterous activity. He then begins to play or rush about, may become over-excited, even intractable, and then it might be difficult to persuade him to sit quietly at a table and do tests of a different type!

The Locomotor Scale gives opportunity to observe certain physical weaknesses or disabilities, or more definite defects of movement in young handicapped children.

Below will be found the entire range of test items for the Loco-

TABLE VII

LOCOMOTOR   SCALE A   From Birth to Eight Years Annual Percentages

Items:	Years: No.	I N=427	II 436	III 327	IV 274	V 285	VI 223	VII 211	VIII 77	Total N 2260
										Passing each item
Year I	I									
Pushes with feet	1	95.1	100							2239
Lifts head when prone	2	92.7	100							2229
Holds head erect	3	92.3	100							2227
Kicks vigorously	4	87.6	100							2207
Lifts head in dorsal position	5	83.4	100							2189
Back firm when held sitting	6	77.8	100							2165
Lifts head and chest when prone	7	75.2	100							2154
Holds head erect continuously	8	74.0	100							2149
Lifts head and shoulders: dorsal	9	65.2	100							2112
Rolls from side to side	10	59.0	100							2085
Crawling Reaction I	11	56.2	100							2073
Sits with slight support	12	52.7	100							2058
Rolls from back to stomach	13	45.4	100	100						2027
Crawling Reaction II	14	40.3	100	100						2005
Sits alone: short time	15	39.6	100	100						2002
Stepping reaction	16	33.5	99.5	100						1974
Can be left sitting on floor	17	27.6	100	100						1951
Stands when held up	18	24.1	99.8	100						1935
Crawling Reaction III	19	22.9	99.3	100						1928
Sits well in a chair	20	20.4	99.5	100						1918
Pulls self up and stands holding	21	14.9	97.9	100						1888
Crawling Reaction IV	22	15.4	96.3	100						1883
Side-steps round inside cot	23	10.8	95.4	100						1859
Can walk when led	24	7.0	94.5	100						1839

(First Six Months) | (Second Six Months)

36

TABLE VII LOCOMOTOR SCALE A — *continued*

	Years: No.	I N=427	II 436	III 327	IV 274	V 285	VI 223	VII 211	VIII 77	Total N 2260
Items:										*Passing each item*
Year II										
Climbs on a low step	II 1	4.2	87.2	100						1795
Stands alone	2	4.2	85.3	100						1787
Takes a few steps alone	3	1.6	77.3	100						1741
Kneels on floor or chair	4	3.7	75.2	100						1741
Climbs steps "up"	5	1.2	75.0	100						1729
Likes pushing pram etc.	6	1.4	73.9	100						1725
Walks alone well	7	.7	71.3	100	100					1711
Stoops	8	.7	65.1	100	100					1684
Develops a quick trot	9	.5	65.1	100	100					1683
Climbs into a low chair	10	.5	62.8	100	100					1672
Can walk backwards	11	0	55.7	100	100					1640
Walks pulling toy on string	12	0	54.1	99.1	100					1630
Climbs stairs up and down	13	0	44.7	98.8	100	100				1588
Runs	14	0	42.6	97.5	100	100				1575
Jumps	15	0	37.6	97.2	100	100				1552
Climbs to stand on a chair	16	0	34.2	95.7	100	100				1532
Walks upstairs	17	0	31.2	96.6	100	100				1522
Can seat self at table	18	0	26.8	92.9	100	100				1491
Walks up and down stairs	19	0	21.3	92.3	100	100				1465
Can kick a ball	20	0	20.2	90.0	100	100				1453
Can jump off a step	21	0	19.5	88.1	100	100				1443
Goes alone on stairs	22	0	18.1	87.5	100	100				1435
Throws ball into basket	23	0	15.4	81.6	97.8	100				1398
Brings chair and seats self	24	0	8.7	61.8	94.5	100				1295

(Third Six Months) | (Fourth Six Months)

37

TABLE VII LOCOMOTOR SCALE A — *continued*

Items:	Years: No.	I N=427	II 436	III 327	IV 274	V 285	VI 223	VII 211	VIII 77	Total N 2260
										Passing each item
Year III										
Jumps off step: both feet together	III 1	0	2.3	67.3	91.6	100	100	100		1282
Can stand on one foot (6 plus secs.)	III 2	0	2.7	53.8	86.5	98.6	100	100		1222
Rises from kneeling	III 3	0	1.8	48.6	87.6	99.3	100	100		1205
Crosses feet and knees sitting	III 4	0	.2	38.5	87.6	97.2	100	100		1155
Can stand and walk on tiptoe	III 5	0	1.1	39.1	77.4	98.2	99.1	100	100	1136
Walks upstairs one foot on each step	III 6	0	.5	26.9	74.5	94.4	98.2	100	100	1071
Year IV										
Can run fast indoors	IV 1		0	15.6	64.6	90.9	97.3	100	100	991
Can ride a tricycle	IV 2		.9	22.0	62.8	84.2	94.6	100	100	987
Marches to music	IV 3		0	7.0	34.7	74.0	93.7	99.1	100	824
Walks a chalk line	IV 4		0	2.8	36.1	79.3	93.3	96.7	100	823
Hops on one foot	IV 5		0	4.0	27.0	70.9	94.2	98.1	100	783
Jumps off two steps	IV 6		0	3.7	31.4	68.1	90.6	96.2	100	774
Year V										
Can run to kick a ball	V 1		0	6.4	30.3	62.8	78.9	94.3	100	735
Walks downstairs 1 foot on each step	V 2		0	4.0	30.3	58.6	79.8	93.8	100	716
Touches toes knees straight	V 3		0	1.5	27.4	70.2	77.1	90.0	93.5	714
Can jump 6" rope feet together	V 4		0	2.4	23.4	61.4	84.3	93.8	100	710
Can climb on or off a bus	V 5		0	2.1	14.2	57.2	81.6	96.2	100	671
Can run upstairs	V 6		0	0	4.4	33.3	64.1	84.4	94.9	501

38

TABLE VII LOCOMOTOR SCALE A — continued

	Years: No.	I N=427	II 436	III 327	IV 274	V 285	VI 223	VII 211	VIII 77	Total N 2260
Items:										Passing each item
Year VI										
Can bounce and catch a ball	VI 1				3.6	30.9	61.9	85.5	93.5	489
Can run fast out of doors	VI 2				2.9	14.3	59.6	96.7	100	463
Can throw up and catch a ball	VI 3				3.6	26.0	59.6	79.6	94.9	461
Can hop-skip 4 plus steps	VI 4				4.0	25.6	58.7	75.4	84.4	439
Jumps off three steps	VI 5				.7	11.9	45.3	60.5	94.8	401
Hopscotch I	VI 6				2.2	15.1	48.9	61.6	83.1	352
Year VII										
Can jump over a rope 10"	VII 1				0	2.5	30.5	73.0	93.5	301
Hop-skips freely indoors	VII 2				0	0	33.2	62.1	72.7	261
Hop-scotch II (2 hopes)	VII 3				0	6.3	31.4	50.7	70.1	249
Can run all round playground	VII 4				0	0	2.7	44.6	87.2	167
Can skip with rope 3 plus	VII 5				.4	2.1	16.6	34.6	62.8	165
Hopscotch III (3 hops)	VII 6				0	.4	12.1	33.2	55.8	141
Year VIII										
Runs downstairs	VIII 1				0	0	4.0	35.1	63.6	132
Jumps off 4 plus steps	VIII 2				0	0	3.1	32.2	67.9	128
Rides a bicycle (2-wheeler)	VIII 3				0	3.5	4.0	26.5	46.2	109
Hopscotch IV (4 hops)	VIII 4				0	0	5.4	22.7	44.2	94
Fast single skipping	VIII 5				0	.4	1.8	19.6	42.8	78
Skips well 12 plus (ordinary skipping)	VIII 6				0	0	1.8	17.5	35.0	68
Year IX										
Hop-skips some distance	IX 1						0	16.6	35.0	62
Rides 2-wheeler with skill	IX 2						0	5.2	13.0	21

See also Part III, Chapter XII

39

motor Scale, from the first month to the ninety-sixth month, and into the ninth year a further four months, to 100 months of mental age.

The total number of test items is 86 in each scale. Of these forty-eight (48) belong to the first two years of the tests, two items for each month of age. Thirty-eight (38) items belong to the extension of each scale, with six items for each year, that allows for two months credit for each item, and the remaining two items, belong to the ninth year.

In Table VII the percentages for all the 86 items of the Locomotor Scale, are given in annual groupings, and are place in strict order of difficulty. It is not, however, necessary for the examiner in applying this scale (or the five others to follow) to keep to any particular order, a good deal of lattitude in testing such young subjects can be allowed. It is usual to begin somewhat below the child's actual age, and work on until he can pass no further items, six[1] failures in succession are usually enough to give the child full opportunity to do all he can.

Scale B: The Personal-Social Scale

Turning now to the Personal-social scale it is often found that certain items of this scale can be introduced in friendly conversation with a child, and scored without him realising that these are tests, or even that he is under examination. Such information for example in Year III or beyond, as knowing his own age, and family name, what young companions he has at school whether he helps in the home and so on, can be gleaned incidentally and recorded provisionally while the child is perhaps engaged in bead threading, or free drawing, or in some other manual task.[2]

Emotionally disturbed children usually do rather badly on this scale, and for two opposite reasons. The over-protected child who is waited on too much in the home, is often slower than others in learning self-help, and in getting practice in dealing with many personal matters such as washing his own hands and face, fastening shoes, etc. On the other hand the neglected child, the one who though he may come from a poor home, or a more prosperous one, does not get enough attention or care from parents who may be too busy perhaps with working outside the home at their occupations

---

[1] This we have called the "Six-item rule" which holds throughout this Scale and in all the five other scales.

[2] The method of testing many of the Personal-Social items, sometimes using implements for table-laying etc., and opportunities for demonstrating putting on shoes, tying laces etc., are fully explained in Part III: Scale B.

PERSONAL-SOCIAL   SCALE B

TABLE VIII

From Birth to Eight Years Annual Percentages

Items:	Years: No.	I N=427	II 436	III 327	IV 274	V 285	VI 223	VII 211	VIII 77	Total N 2260
										Passing each item
Year I										
Quieted when picked up	I 1	97.9	100							2251
Enjoys bath	2	92.7	100							2230
Smiling	3	88.3	100							2210
Visually recognises mother	4	87.3	100							2206
Follows a moving person	5	83.8	100							2191
Returns glance with smiling	6	81.0	100							2179
Frolics when played with	7	68.3	100							2125
Resists adult taking ring	8	67.2	100							2120
Anticipatory movements	9	64.8	100							2110
Turns head to person talking	10	63.9	100							2106
Stretches to be taken	11	48.9	100							2042
Drinks from a cup	12	48.4	99.7	100						2039
Manipulates cup and spoon in play	13	47.1	100	100						2034
Knows strangers from friends	14	41.9	99.7	100						2021
Prompt reaction to situations	15	40.9	100	100						2008
Displeased if toy taken away	16	30.7	98.9	100						1959
Helps to hold cup for drinking	17	29.3	99.1	100						1954
Reacts to mirror image	18	24.6	97.9	100						1929
Gives affection	19	19.6	98.4	100						1910
Finger feeds	20	18.0	98.2	100						1902
Waves "bye-bye"	21	16.2	96.6	100						1887
Plays with cup, spoon and saucer	22	16.2	93.4	100						1883
Plays "Pat-a-cake"	23	12.2	92.4	100						1852
Obeys simple requests	24	8.4	93.6	100						1841

(First Six Months) | (Second Six Months)

41

Table VIII PERSONAL-SOCIAL SCALE B — *continued*

Items:	Years: No.	I N=427	II 436	III 327	IV 274	V 285	VI 223	VII 211	VIII 77	Total N 2260
										Passing each item
Year II	II									
Puts objects in and out of cup	1	8.4	92.4	100						1836
Tries to help with dressing	2	7.0	89.4	100						1817
Can hold cup himself when drinking	3	4.2	84.4	100	100					1783
Uses spoon: spills some	4	4.2	84.4	100	100					1783
Shows shoes on request	5	2.1	71.8	100	100					1718
	6	.5	60.6	99.1	100					1660
Tries to turn door knob	7	.7	53.7	99.4	100					1652
Likes adult to show book	8	.2	56.6	99.1	100					1642
Manages cup well half-full	9	.2	54.3	97.7	100					1634
Can take off socks and shoes	10	.2	50.2	98.2	100					1611
Uses spoon well	11	.2	50.2	98.2	100					1611
	12	0	47.0	98.2	100					1596
Knows parts of body (1)	13	0	45.9	96.9	100					1587
Cleanliness: asks	14	.5	45.2	96.6	100					1585
Bowel control	15	0	35.8	92.9	100					1530
Knows parts of body (2)	16	0	32.8	94.8	100	100				1523
Tries to tell experiences	17	0	27.5	92.0	99.3	100				1489
Bladder control by day	18	0	26.8	92.0	100	100				1488
Knows parts of body (3)	19	0	25.7	92.9	100	100				1486
Asks for things at table	20	0	23.9	90.5	98.9	100				1467
Knows parts of body (4)	21	0	21.3	89.9	100	100				1457
Can open door himself	22	0	17.2	88.1	99.3	100	100			1431
Helps actively with dressing	23	0	15.4	85.9	100	100	100			1418
Begins to co-operate in play with other children	24	0	12.2	59.9	90.9	100	100			1294

(Third Six Months) | (Fourth Six Months)

42

TABLE VIII PERSONAL-SOCIAL SCALE B — *continued*

Items:	Years: No.	I N=427	II 436	III 327	IV 274	V 285	VI 223	VII 211	VIII 77	Total N 2260
										Passing each item
Year III										
Gives first name	III 1	0	7.6	59.3	92.7	98.9	100	100		1274
Uses spoon and fork	III 2	0	6.2	54.4	77.7	93.7	100	100		1196
Puts away toys	III 3	0	7.1	41.9	80.7	90.9	99.5	100		1158
Knows own sex	III 4	0	.7	36.1	82.5	97.9	99.1	100		1135
Can undo buttons	III 5	0	.7	35.7	79.9	97.5	99.5	100		1127
Gives family name	III 6	0	1.1	34.8	70.8	93.7	99.1	100		1089
Year IV										
Can do up buttons	IV 1		.4	20.2	67.5	90.2	99.5	99.5	100	1019
Can put on shoes and socks	IV 2		0	19.5	57.3	78.9	92.8	99.1	100	950
Knows age (years)	IV 3		.2	5.2	47.8	78.6	91.0	96.6	100	858
Plays well with other children	IV 4		0	9.2	48.2	73.7	92.4	95.7	96.0	854
Helps to lay table	IV 5		0	5.8	34.7	61.1	88.3	95.7	96.1	761
Can undress self	IV 6		0	1.5	24.8	63.5	86.1	97.1	100	728
Year V										
Washes own hands and face	V 1		0	5.2	27.7	52.9	77.5	90.5	93.7	680
Gives address (2)	V 2		.2	5.8	24.1	47.4	70.9	88.6	98.7	642
Uses knife and fork fairly well	V 3		0	1.8	13.8	52.9	78.5	91.5	98.7	639
Can dress and undress self	V 4		0	0	12.4	48.8	70.9	95.3	100	611
Can fasten buckles	V 5		0	1.2	13.1	46.6	72.2	89.5	93.7	596
Manages top coat unaided	V 6		0	0	7.3	40.0	66.4	91.5	100	552

TABLE VIII PERSONAL-SOCIAL SCALE B — *continued*

Items:	Years: No.	I N=427	II 436	III 327	IV 274	V 285	VI 223	VII 211	VIII 77	Total N 2260
										Passing each item
Year VI										
Has a special playmate	VI 1			1.5	16.8	35.8	67.3	83.4	88.3	547
Can tie a single knot	VI 2		0	0	4.4	36.1	71.3	91.9	96.1	542
Can go alone on errands	VI 3		0	2.1	9.9	30.5	55.2	69.7	85.7	457
(credit 2 points)	VI 4		0	2.1	9.9	30.5	55.2	69.7	85.7	457
Can brush and comb hair	VI 5		0	0	10.6	29.1	41.2	60.2	81.8	397
Knows full address	VI 6		0	0	4.0	17.5	24.2	65.9	77.9	314
Year VII										
Can tie a bow-knot (1 loop)	VII 1			0	0	6.0	30.9	59.1	80.5	274
Knife and fork: cuts own meat	VII 2			0	.7	12.6	33.2	48.3	77.9	273
Shoes: can tie laces	VII 3				0	13.9	21.9	56.9	75.3	238
Efficient and competent at table	VII 4				0	8.8	24.6	39.8	59.8	210
(credit as 2 points)	VII 5				0	8.8	24.6	39.8	59.8	210
Can tie a bow-knot (2 loops)	VII 6				0	2.1	16.6	48.8	62.3	194
Year VIII										
Can dress and undress completely	VIII 1				0	.4	12.1	45.9	64.9	175
Has a special school friend	VIII 2				0	.3	9.0	42.1	64.9	159
Takes full responsibility for hair	VIII 3				0	0	8.1	35.5	51.9	133
(credit 2 points)	VIII 4				0	0	8.1	35.5	51.9	133
Knows own birthday, day and month	VIII 5				0	1.4	3.6	32.2	57.1	122
Can lay a table	VIII 6				0	0	2.2	19.4	36.1	74
Year IX										
Can lay table without help or sup'v'n.	IX 1					0	1.8	17.1	27.2	61
Knows date of birth	IX 2					0	.4	1.0	15.6	15

44

or professions, and the child may become unhappy or difficult in one way or another.

The very poor child or one from an unstable or impoverished family may also fail on Scale B, but where there is normal affection these causes may not operate. Such facts and circumstances may affect the test result of such a child. It is of course also true that unhappiness or maladjustment can affect results in every one of the scales in some degree, but Scale B will usually show these effects more definitely than other scales. All such observations can help our decisions or conclusions about a child and contribute to the findings, when the total picture is complete. The sub-scale in which the child fails most markedly can usually give the clue to the nature of the problem, where one exists.

Above will be found the percentage table of all the test items of Scale B, where also the details of the tests are listed.

Scale C: Hearing and Speech, and General Verbal Ability

Scale C is the most intellectual of the scales. Placed centrally in the profile it gives the impression of the able child's capacity at its peak, and in the case of a mentally slow child the result on Scale C may lie in a trough in the profile. A deep trough at C may indicate a degree of deafness, or slight or more severe hearing loss.

One of the most important functions of this profile technique is the opportunity it gives even where the child is very young, for the examiner to locate any speech slowness or impairment, that could be associated with hearing loss. Again, the items of this scale listed below give opportunity for the study of the growth and development of language in children from birth onwards. The gradual acquisition of sounds in early infancy, then monosyllables, two-syllable babble, and the earliest learning of words, have been examined in detail and described in the earlier volume.[1] When we come to the study of older children it is the gradual enrichment of vocabulary, the use of different parts of speech, learning to use sentences, and to develop paragraphs of decription in relation to pictures, and so on. All such items occur in this scale and the more intellectual and verbal children do well on Scale C. Here again a child may show a high peak at the centre of the profile due to a special interest or skill at spoken language and comprehension, and yet do much less well at handwork on the one hand or physical prowess on the other.

These are individual differences that lie within the normal range

[1] See "The Abilities of Babies", Chapter XIII.

TABLE IX

HEARING AND SPEECH SCALE C From Birth to Eight Years Annua l Percentages

	Items:	Years: No.	I N=427	II 436	III 327	IV 274	V 285	VI 223	VII 211	VIII 77	Total N 2260
(First Six Months)	**Year I**										*Passing each item*
	Startled by sounds	I 1	96.9	100							2247
	Vocalisation other than crying	2	95.3	100							2240
	Listens to bell	3	90.9	100							2221
	Searches for sound visually	4	85.7	100							2199
	Makes 2 plus different sounds	5	80.3	100							2176
	Listens to music	6	77.0	100							2162
	Seaches for sound, head movements	7	74.5	100							2151
	Listens to tuning fork	8	64.6	100							2109
	Turns head to bell	9	62.3	100							2099
	Coos or stops crying on hearing music	10	58.8	100							2084
	Babbles to persons	11	57.8	100							2080
	Makes 4 plus different sounds	12	56.4	99.5	100						2072
(Second Six Months)	Responds when called	13	48.5	100	100						2040
	Two-syllable babble	14	48.7	99.5	100						2039
	Listens to conversations	15	37.7	100	100						1994
	Babbled phrases 4 plus syllables	16	31.1	99.3	100						1963
	Says Mama, Dada etc. 1 word clear	17	28.1	97.7	100						1943
	Listens to stop watch	18	26.9	97.5	100						1937
	Rings the bell	19	20.3	96.6	100						1905
	Shakes head for "No"	20	19.7	96.8	100						1903
	Says two clear words	21	18.7	95.0	100						1891
	Babbled sentences 6 plus syllables	22	14.8	95.9	100						1878
	Babbled monologue when alone	23	11.5	94.0	100						1856
	Three clear words	24	9.8	90.4	100						1833

TABLE IX HEARING AND SPEECH SCALE C — *continued*

Items:	Years: No.	I N=427	II 436	III 327	IV 274	V 285	VI 223	VII 211	VIII 77	Total N 2260 *Passing each item*
Year II										
(Third Six Months)										
Looks at pictures for a few seconds	1	6.5	90.8	100	100					1821
Tries definitely to sing	2	6.1	84.8	100	100					1793
Knows own name	3	5.2	85.1	100	100					1790
Likes rhymes and jingles	4	3.3	76.8	99.7	100					1745
Looks at pictures with interest	5	0	73.8	100	100					1719
Uses 4 clear words	6	1.4	71.8	100	100					1716
One object in box identified	7	.2	60.3	99.7	100					1660
Uses 5 clear words	8	0	57.3	100	100					1647
Long babbled conversations	9	0	57.3	99.4	100					1645
Enjoys picture book	10	.5	55.9	99.4	100					1638
Uses 6 or 7 clear words	11	.5	54.8	99.4	100					1636
Two objects in box identified	12	0	47.5	97.6	100					1596
(Fourth Six Months)										
Uses 9 clear words	13	0	41.2	96.3	100	100				1565
Four objects identified	14	0	35.1	96.0	100	100				1537
Picture vocabulary 1	15	0	33.5	94.8	100	100				1526
Uses 12 clear words	16	0	33.0	94.8	100	100				1524
Word combinations	17	0	30.9	93.2	100	100				1510
Picture vocabulary 2	18	0	25.0	92.7	100	100				1482
Uses 20 plus clear words	19	0	22.2	90.2	99.2	100	100			1460
Eight objects identified	20	0	20.2	92.4	99.6	100	100			1459
Listens to stories	21	0	21.3	90.2	99.2	100	100			1456
Names 4 objects in box	22	0	20.0	91.7	99.6	100	100			1456
Picture vocabulary 4	23	0	16.5	88.4	99.2	100	100			1429
Uses sentences of 4 syllables	24	0	13.8	76.7	96.0	100	100			1370

47

TABLE IX HEARING AND SPEACH SCALE C — *continued*

Items:	Years: No.	I N=427	II 436	III 327	IV 274	V 285	VI 223	VII 211	VIII 77	Total N 2260
										Passing each item
Year III										
Names 12 toys in box	III 1		7.6	74.6	95.6	99.6	100	100	100	1334
Picture vocabulary 12	III 2		3.2	60.2	94.5	95.4	99.5	100	100	1252
Defines by use: 2 plus	III 3		1.4	24.2	74.1	95.4	97.3	99.5	100	1060
Repeats a six-syllable sentence	III 4		.2	24.5	72.9	92.6	99.1	99.5	100	1053
Uses 2 descriptive words	III 5		1.6	27.2	61.3	90.5	100	100	100	1033
Talks in sentences (6 plus)	III 6		.9	24.5	62.8	87.0	92.4	100	100	998
Year IV										
Names 6 objects in picture	IV 1		1.6	20.8	58.0	82.5	94.2	99.5	100	966
Names 17-18 objects in box	IV 2		2.1	25.4	57.3	77.9	90.6	96.2	100	953
Uses personal pronouns, 2	IV 3		0	15.9	46.7	80.5	93.7	99.5	100	905
Comprehension 2 plus items	IV 4		0	7.3	52.3	87.0	96.8	99.5	97.4	889
Picture vocabulary 18	IV 5		0	10.1	44.2	78.6	87.8	92.9	100	847
Names six colours	IV 6		0	2.1	30.6	55.4	86.7	94.3	98.7	716
Year V										
Defines by use: 6 plus	V 1		0	2.7	21.5	59.6	82.0	94.8	100	698
Opposites: 2 plus	V 2		0	.9	20.8	61.0	83.4	92.4	97.4	690
Materials: 2 plus	V 3		0	.3	13.5	59.6	85.2	93.8	97.4	671
Repeats sentences: 10 syllables	V 4		0	.6	14.2	47.4	79.8	85.8	89.6	604
Picture Description: 1 sentence	V 5		0	2.4	13.1	36.5	68.6	82.4	93.5	547
Names 12 plus objects in picture	V 6		0	1.8	9.1	40.0	64.5	77.2	94.8	525

Year III | Year IV | Year V

48

TABLE IX HEARING AND SPEECH SCALE C — *continued*

Items:	Years: No.	I N=427	II 436	III 327	IV 274	V 285	VI 223	VII 211	VIII 77	Total N 2260
										Passing each item
Year VI										
Talks in sentences: 10 plus syllables	VI 1		0	1.8	10.6	34.0	51.5	92.9	100	520
Comprehension: 4 plus	VI 2		0	.6	12.8	34.4	60.1	83.9	89.6	515
Uses 6 descriptive words	VI 3		0	.6	5.5	20.3	62.3	91.9	100	485
Knows capital letters 10 plus	VI 4		0	0	1.1	10.2	35.4	74.9	92.2	340
Personal pronouns 6 plus	VI 5		0	.6	2.9	6.7	31.8	78.7	89.6	335
Names 10 colours	VI 6		0	.9	5.1	13.3	35.8	63.9	81.8	333
Year VII										
Repeats 16 syllables	VII 1			0	3.3	16.1	33.6	52.6	66.2	292
Picture description 3	VII 2			0	3.3	9.1	39.4	46.9	80.5	284
Knows 20 capital letters	VII 3			0	.7	5.6	22.4	60.2	87.0	262
Similarities: 1	VII 4			0	0	3.1	28.7	55.4	68.8	243
Differences: 2	VII 5			0	0	4.6	23.3	55.9	70.1	237
Capital letters: 26	VII 6			0	.3	3.1	13.9	39.8	75.3	183
Year VIII										
Picture description 4	VIII 1				0	3.1	16.6	39.3	66.2	180
Similarites: 2	VIII 2				0	1.1	19.3	39.8	51.9	170
Comprehension: 6	VIII 3				0	3.1	11.2	43.6	51.9	166
Differences: 3	VIII 4				0	1.1	9.8	35.5	51.9	140
Similarities: 3	VIII 5				0	.4	9.0	25.1	26.3	102
Opposites: 3	VIII 6				0	1.1	5.8	17.5	26.0	73
Year IX										
Differences 4 — credit as	IX 1				0	.4	3.1	14.7	16.9	52
Differences 4 — 2 items	IX 2				0	.4	3.1	14.7	16.9	52

49

and are met with constantly when testing in schools, and give scope for a fuller understanding of a particular child's mentality and interests.

A high Scale C result can also often be found in profoundly afflicted children, where the handicap is largely physical. In this connection the education and future treatment of thalidomide children, come much into mind.

In Table IX will be found the full range of tests for Scale C, together with the percentages.[1]

Scale D: Hand and Eye Co-ordination

This Scale consists of a similar list of items to the other scales, but now relating to the handwork and visual ability of the child under test. It has also been similarly standardised, with the same number of items as the other scales. This scale gives the examiner opportunity to observe more closely the *hands* of the child. Manual dexterity, persistence in a task, careful and diligent work, are seen in many children. Negatively, the awkward movements and weak hands of the spastic child, the fumbling slowness of the mongol child, and other peculiarities can be observed. Left-handedness should always be noted. Visual difficulties are immediately apparent.

All such matters coming under observation help the diagnostic picture and increase the psychologists understanding of the child's difficulties, if any.

The activity of drawing features largely in this scale, and if the child can be given enough time, in addition to the formal drawing tests, for some free drawing expression, together with verbal description of what he has drawn, interesting aspects of a problem sometimes emerge. The more formal drawings of geometrical shapes, provide another series for the study of the child's conception of space and form relations. In fact drawing, both formal and more free, can throw light on a child's personality in ways not otherwise easily observed.

The percentage table of Scale D, together with the details of the items of the Hand and Eye Scale are given below in Table X.

Note: For the method of applying details of Scale D, see Part III, Chapter XV.

Scale E: A Scale of Performance Tests

This Scale is very largely a scale of performance tests. These are

[1] For the method of applying Scale C see Part III, Chapter XIV of this book.

TABLE X

HAND AND EYE CO-ORDINATION   SCALE D   From Birth to Eight Years

Annual Percentages

Items:	Years: No.	I N=427	II 436	III 327	IV 274	V 285	VI 223	VII 211	VIII 77	Total N 2260
										Passing each item
Year I	I									
Follows a moving light with eyes	1	98.4	100							2253
Looks at ring or toy momentarily	2	97.7	100							2250
Follows moving ring horizontally	3	91.1	100							2222
Follows bell-ring vertically	4	87.8	100							2208
Follows bell-ring in a circle	5	80.6	100							2177
Glances from one object to another	6	79.4	100							2172
Watches object pulled along by string	7	76.8	100							2161
Visually explores new environment	8	72.6	100							2143
Reaches for ring and grasps	9	65.8	100							2114
Secures dangling ring	10	57.8	100							2080
Hands explore table surface	11	53.6	100							2062
Plays with ring, shaking bells etc.	12	52.7	100							2058
Looks for fallen object	13	43.3	99.5	100						2017
Strikes one object with another	14	42.4	100	100						2014
F'finger and thumb partly specialised	15	37.7	99.3	100						1991
Secures ring by means of string	16	33.9	99.1	100						1974
Fine prehension	17	23.4	99.1	100						1929
Dangles ring by string	18	22.2	96.8	100						1915
Throws objects	19	17.6	98.6	100						1902
Thumb opposition complete	20	15.5	97.5	100						1888
Can point with index finger	21	14.8	95.2	100						1875
Interested in motor car	22	14.5	95.4	100						1875
Can hold pencil as if to mark on paper	23	10.3	94.9	100						1855
Likes holding little toys	24	6.8	92.7	100						1830

(First Six Months)

(Second Six Months)

TABLE X   HAND AND EYE CO-ORDINATION   SCALE D — *continued*

Items:	Years: No.	I N=427	II 436	III 327	IV 274	V 285	VI 223	VII 211	VIII 77	Total N 2260
										Passing each item
Year II	II									
Uses pencil on paper a little	1	4.7	87.8	100						1800
Shows preference for one hand	2	5.9	81.4	100						1777
Plays rolling ball	3	2.8	81.2	100						1763
Can hold 4 cubes in hands at once	4	4.2	79.8	100	100					1763
Plays pushing little cars along	5	3.7	78.2	100	100					1754
Places one brick upon another	6	1.6	77.8	100	100					1743
Tower of 2 bricks:— shown	7	1.2	69.9	99.7	100					1706
Pulls paper or cloth to get toy	8	1.2	62.4	98.8	100					1670
Scribbles more freely	9	1.2	56.7	98.5	100					1644
Constructive play with boxes— or other materials	10	0	56.2	98.8	100					1638
	11	0	56.2	98.8	100					1638
Tower of 3 bricks	12	0	55.7	98.2	100					1634
Can throw a ball	13	.5	54.1	98.5	100					1634
(credit as 2)	14	.5	54.1	98.5	100					1634
Tower of 4 bricks	15	0	38.3	95.1	100					1548
Enjoys vigorous straight scribble	16	0	37.2	94.2	100					1540
Can pour water neatly	17	0	29.1	95.7	100					1510
Tower of 5 bricks	18	0	23.4	92.7	100					1473
Circular scribble in imitation	19	0	19.5	90.2	100					1450
Train of three bricks	20	0	16.3	86.8	100					1423
	21	0	16.3	86.8	100					1423
Making a brick or toy walk	22	0	17.4	81.7	100					1408
Tower of 6 or 7 bricks	23	0	13.8	80.7	100					1393
Makes perpendicular stroke	24	0	16.9	74.3	100					1384

(Third Six Months)

(Fourth Six Months)

52

TABLE X   HAND AND EYE CO-ORDINATION   SCALE D — *continued*

Items:	Years: No.	I N=427	II 436	III 327	IV 274	V 285	VI 223	VII 211	VIII 77	Total N 2260
										Passing each item
Year III										
Horizontal stroke	III 1	0	11.2	68.5	98.2	100	100	100		1338
Threads 6 beads	III 2	0	2.1	56.6	94.2	99.6	99.6	100		1246
Tower of 8 plus bricks	III 3	0	4.6	51.9	92.7	98.2	100	100	100	1235
Handles scissors: tries to cut	III 4	0	.9	40.7	89.1	97.5	99.6	100	100	1169
Copies circle: primitive model	III 5	0	1.1	30.9	77.0	95.1	100	100	100	1099
Copies cross: recognisable	III 6	0	0	22.0	77.4	95.8	100	100	100	1068
Year IV										
Folds a 4″ square once	IV 1	0	1.6	24.8	72.3	94.7	100	99.5	100	1066
Threads 12 beads (not pattern)	IV 2	0	.9	16.8	57.7	91.6	99.6	99.5	100	987
Can cut square into 2 pieces	IV 3	0	0	3.4	37.2	79.6	94.2	95.2	100	828
Folds 4″ square twice	IV 4	0	.2	8.3	36.8	75.1	92.4	95.2	98.7	826
Copies ladder	IV 5	0	0	.2	27.4	77.5	96.9	99.1	100	800
Draws 'a man' recognisable	IV 6	0	0	4.3	24.1	60.4	88.8	97.6	100	733
Year V										
Draws a good cross	V 1		0	3.7	20.8	60.7	89.2	96.2	100	721
Circle, good shape and closed	V 2		0	2.1	29.9	53.7	79.8	92.9	98.7	692
Square, recognisable	V 3		0	0	16.1	60.4	85.2	96.7	98.7	686
Window, Stage 1	V 4		0	0	3.3	33.7	81.6	93.4	93.5	556
House (a)	V 5		0	0	6.9	30.2	72.6	95.2	100	545
Scissors: can strip edge of paper	V 6		0	0	7.7	43.5	60.1	82.5	92.2	524

TABLE X HAND AND EYE CO-ORDINATION SCALE D — *continued*

	Items:	Years: No.	I N=427	II 436	III 327	IV 274	V 285	VI 223	VII 211	VIII 77	Total N 2260
											Passing each item
Year VI	**Year VI**										
	Threads 12 beads to pattern	VI 1			0	5.5	26.3	65.9	83.9	92.2	488
	Triangle (a)	VI 2			0	4.4	18.2	62.3	87.2	87.4	462
	Draws 'a man': Stage 2	VI 3			.3	4.7	22.1	51.5	66.8	87.0	400
	Makes 3 letters	VI 4			0	2.2	18.9	34.5	78.7	96.1	377
	Can write or print first name	VI 5			0	.4	8.8	44.8	78.2	94.8	364
	House (b)	VI 6			0	1.4	10.8	40.8	66.3	92.2	337
Year VII	**Year VII**										
	Copies a square (b)	VII 1			0	1.1	12.6	38.1	67.8	71.4	322
	Draws ladder (b)	VII 2			0	.7	13.3	30.9	60.2	84.4	301
	Draws diamond (a)	VII 3			0	0	3.9	24.2	63.0	81.8	261
	Draws triangle (b)	VII 4			0	0	3.9	24.2	58.3	85.7	254
	Can write figures to 9	VII 5			0	0	1.1	18.4	58.8	85.7	234
	Can write full name	VII 6			0	0	.7	19.9	52.6	81.8	220
Year VIII	**Year VIII**										
	Makes letters (10)	VIII 1			0	0	4.6	11.6	50.2	84.4	210
	Draws window: Stage 2	VIII 2			0	1.4	7.0	24.2	37.4	57.1	201
	'Man': Stage 3	VIII 3			0	.4	2.8	18.8	27.5	42.8	142
	Diamond, good shape and drawing {	VIII 4				0	.4	7.6	27.0	42.8	108
		VIII 5				0	.4	7.6	27.0	42.8	108
	Letters (24)	VIII 6				0	.7	3.1	23.2	55.8	101
Year IX	**Year IX**										
	Draws a house: Stage (c) and well {	IX 1						4.9	10.4	29.9	56
	drawn	IX 2						4.9	10.4	29.9	56

54

new tests original to this work. The children enjoy handling the materials and doing the tests.

Performance tests enable the examiner to observe and measure skill in manipulation, speed of working and precision. Certain tests are timed with a stop-watch. The children like this scale. The eagerness and persistence of clever children is very delightful to observe. This scale also supplements Scale D in some ways and gives opportunity for observing the ways in which slow and handicapped children yet find pleasure in doing these tests. Although they may not score very highly, the results are often of great value, in helping the examiner to understand a particular child's difficulties. Here is something interesting that a child will not mind trying to do. The materials are attractive even to the slowest child, and the simplest ones are used with babies under a year old, and the more difficult ones tax the ingenuity of the eight-year-olds.

The percentage table for Scale E is given below, together with the details of the tests as before.

See Part II, Chapter XVI for the method of applying Scale E.

Scale F: Practical Reasoning

Scale F begins at the third year. This scale provides opportunity for the recording of the earliest indications of arithmetical comprehension in these young children, and realisation of the simplest practical problems. Higher up the scale more complicated exercises give the bright or somewhat older child, scope for showing what he can achieve in this field.

Although the series of items begins at year three, where the required 50% of the children do some of the tests, we found it necessary to go down into the top half of the second year to test children between 18 and 24 months of age, and here we found a small percentage of babies who could respond successfully to items involving recognition of differences of size, selecting the "bigger one" of two objects, recognising one or more coins, and even a beginning at counting and repeating numbers. But for the vast majority of babies under two years old, these tests are too difficult and therefore unsuitable. The tests of Scale F range up to eight years of mental age, and give scope for the testing of the capacity to grasp and resolve many practical problems and simple arithmetical problems.

The question is sometimes raised as to whether this Scale (Scale F) does indeed measure any capacity to reason about practical problems in such young children. It is the writer's view, that most intellectual

TABLE XI
PERFORMANCE TESTS   SCALE E   From Birth to Eight Years
Annual Percentages

Items:	Years: No.	I N = 427	II 436	III 327	IV 274	V 285	VI 223	VII 211	VIII 77	Total N 2260
										Passing each item
Year I										
Reacts to *paper I*, generalised movement	1	95.7	100							2242
Hand goes to mouth	2	94.1	100							2235
Shows energetic arm movements	3	91.8	100							2225
Holds rod	4	85.0	100							2196
Reacts to *paper II*, vigorous head turning	5	83.8	100							2191
Plays with own fingers	6	78.9	100							2170
Resists rod withdrawal	7	73.8	100							2148
Clasps cube put in hand	8	73.5	100							2147
Reacts to *paper III*, pulls it away	9	56.7	100							2075
Shows interest in box	10	55.7	100							2071
Holds 2 cubes	11	55.5	100							2070
Takes cube or toy from table	12	52.9	100							2059
Passes toy from hand to hand	13	47.1	99.8	100						2033
Drops one cube for third	14	42.9	99.5	100						2014
Manipulates 2 objects at once	15	40.5	98.8	100						2005
Reacts to *paper IV*, plays with	16	35.6	99.5	100						1983
Lifts inverted cup in search of toy	17	29.3	98.6	100						1952
Rattles box	18	25.5	98.6	100						1936
Lifts lid from box	19	18.5	97.7	100						1902
Clicks 2 bricks together	20	17.8	95.4	100						1889
Tries to take cubes out of box	21	15.0	93.8	100						1871
Finds toy under cup	22	12.4	96.6	100						1870
Accepts third cube without dropping	23	14.1	92.0	100						1858
Manipulates box, lid and cubes	24	10.3	95.0	100						1855

(First Six Months) — (Second Six Months)

TABLE XI PERFORMANCE TESTS SCALE E — *continued*

Items:	Years: No.	I N=427	II 436	III 327	IV 274	V 285	VI 223	VII 211	VIII 77	Total N 2260
										Passing each item
Year II	II									
(Third Six Months)										
Removes both cubes from box, shown	1	6.8	90.6	100						1821
Unwraps and finds toy or cube	2	6.3	84.4	100						1792
One-circle board: two trials	3	3.5	84.4	100						1780
Opens 2 boxes	4	1.2	83.7	100						1767
Puts cubes in and out of boxes in play	5	.7	76.8	100						1735
Puts 2 cubes back into box	6	.2	75.5	100						1727
Two-circle board, one in	7	.7	73.2	100	100					1719
Square board: two trials	8	.5	64.7	100	100					1681
Two-circle board, two in	9	0	64.4	99.7	100					1677
Can put lid back on box	10	.2	57.6	99.4	100					1647
Three-hole board, one in	11	0	55.0	99.4	100					1635
Puts 2 cubes in box, lid on, complete	12	0	46.6	97.9	100					1593
(Fourth Six Months)										
Circle and square board together	13	0	45.6	97.9	100					1589
Three-hole board, two in	14	0	40.8	97.9	100					1568
Three-hole board, three in	15	0	34.2	96.9	100					1536
Two-circle board rotated	16	0	23.6	87.8	100	100				1460
Circle and square board, rotated	17	0	20.2	82.9	99.6	100				1428
Credit 2 points	18	0	20.2	82.9	99.6	100				1428
Assembles three boxes	19	0	18.1	85.3	98.9	100				1425
Credit 2 points	20	0	18.1	85.3	98.9	100				1425
Can open screw toy	21	0	18.1	79.5	98.9	100	100			1406
Credit 2 points	22	0	18.1	79.5	98.9	100	100			1406
Three-hole board, rotated	23	0	9.4	70.3	98.2	100	100			1336
Credit 2 points	24	0	9.4	70.3	98.2	100	100			1336

57

TABLE XI PERFORMANCE TESTS SCALE E — continued

Items:	Years: No.	I N=427	II 436	III 327	IV 274	V 285	VI 223	VII 211	VIII 77	Total N 2260
										Passing each item
Year III										
Re-assembles screw toy	III 1	0	7.8	59.6	92.7	97.2	100	99.5	100	1268
Returns 9 bricks and lid to box	III 2	0	6.4	54.4	90.1	97.5	100	100	100	1242
Four squares board (2 trials, 1 min.)	III 3	0	1.6	46.5	88.7	97.5	100	100	100	1191
Six hole board in 1 minute	III 4	0	2.1	43.7	87.2	98.2	100	99.5	98.7	1180
4 squares board in 40 seconds	III 5	0	.7	40.1	85.8	96.5	99.6	99.1	100	1152
Six-holes board in 40 seconds	III 6	0	.7	26.0	71.1	96.1	99.1	98.6	98.7	1062
Year IV										
Returns 9 bricks to box, 40 seconds	IV 1	0	3.9	19.6	60.5	87.7	96.4	100	100	1001
Builds bridge with boxes	IV 2	0	.7	13.4	66.4	90.2	97.8	100	100	992
Assembles boxes by colour	IV 3	0	.7	23.9	57.3	87.4	95.9	98.6	100	986
Four-squares board, 15 seconds	IV 4		0	15.6	43.8	75.8	86.1	94.3	94.8	852
Train under bridge, successfully	IV 5		0	4.0	36.5	72.6	86.5	90.0	94.8	776
Eleven-hole board, 60 seconds	IV 6		0	1.5	22.3	64.2	87.8	94.3	94.8	717
Year V										
Six-hole board in 20 seconds	V 1		0	.3	21.9	59.3	86.1	92.4	97.4	692
Builds bridge, superior	V 2		0	1.2	20.1	60.3	80.2	73.0	93.5	636
Pattern making No. 2, 60 seconds	V 3		0	0	11.3	46.7	81.6	93.8	96.1	618
Builds gate to model	V 4		0	.3	15.3	46.7	69.5	84.4	87.0	576
Pattern making No. 2, 40 seconds	V 5		0	0	6.2	38.2	75.3	91.0	93.5	558
Pattern making No. 5, 60 seconds	V 6		0	0	3.3	27.7	64.1	92.8	94.8	500

Year III | Year IV | Year V

58

TABLE XI PERFORMANCE TESTS SCALE E — *continued*

Items:	Years: No.	I N=427	II 436	III 327	IV 274	V 285	VI 223	VII 211	VIII 77	Total N 2260 *Passing each item*
Year VI										
Eleven-hole board in 40 seconds	VI 1			0	3.3	28.1	57.4	81.0	89.6	457
Pattern making No. 5 in 40 seconds	VI 2			0	1.8	16.1	55.6	86.2	92.2	430
Ten brick memory stairs	VI 3			0	2.2	23.8	48.9	74.9	83.1	405
Pattern making No. 3 in 60 seconds	VI 4			0	.4	13.7	48.0	76.3	88.3	376
Returns 9 bricks to box, 20 seconds	VI 5			0	5.1	19.3	41.2	72.0	77.9	373
Pattern making No. 4, 60 seconds	VI 6			0	.7	11.9	41.7	76.8	91.6	361
Year VII										
Pattern making No. 3 in 40 seconds	VII 1			0	0	6.7	33.2	65.4	81.8	294
Pattern making No. 4 in 40 seconds	VII 2			0	0	5.9	29.6	63.5	81.8	280
Four-squares board, 7 seconds	VII 3			0	2.5	10.9	30.0	54.0	61.0	267
Eleven-hole board, 30 seconds	VII 4			0	0	5.9	24.2	59.7	61.0	244
Pattern making No. 2, 20 seconds	VII 5			0	0	5.3	26.4	48.3	72.7	232
Pattern making No. 3, 30 seconds	VII 6			0	0	1.1	19.7	50.2	71.4	208
Year VIII										
Pattern making No. 4 in 30 seconds	VIII 1			0	0	.4	17.0	40.7	64.9	175
Six-hole board in 10 seconds	VIII 2			0	.4	7.0	13.0	31.7	45.4	153
Pattern making No. 5 in 20 seconds	VIII 3			0	0	.4	9.0	30.3	53.2	126
Returns 9 bricks to box, 15 seconds	VIII 4				0	2.5	10.3	28.4	37.7	119
Pattern making No. 2, 15 seconds	VIII 5				0	2.1	7.6	20.4	32.4	91
Pattern making No. 8 in 20 seconds	VIII 6				0	0	3.5	15.6	32.4	66
Year IX										
Pattern making No. 4 in 20 seconds	IX 1				0	.4	4.9	13.3	24.7	59
Pattern making No. 5 in 15 seconds	IX 2				0	0	1.8	9.0	15.6	35

59

abilities are present, as it were "in embryo", even in the youngest child, long before he can express his ideas verbally, provided he is a normal child capable of looking, listening and learning.

Considering the earliest beginnings of mathematical reasoning, and of cognition as such, takes one back to first principles. The writer had the great privilege of working many years ago, in the Department of Psychology at University College, London, in the days when Professor C. Spearman was head of that department. In two important books "The Abilities of Man"[1], and "The Principles of Cognition"[1] he laid the foundations of our knowledge concerning thinking, and shows the way the mind works in its apprehension of environment. It has been the writer's pleasure as well her task during all the years since then to study and enjoy children, especially young children, their behaviour, their fantasies, and the way they think, and learn.

It might be relevant therefore to look again at the "Principles of Cognition" as described by Spearman in those early days, when methods of mental measurement were first being discussed. These are:

1. The capacity to become aware of what Spearman called "fundaments", that is the simplest of objects, or elements, or qualities in objects.

2. The capacity to relate simple fundaments together or discover the relationships between them and

3. The eduction of correlates.

This last is the capacity, given one fundament and given the relation between it and another fundament, to discover or name the second fundament. This "eduction of a correlate" is a somewhat more difficult task.

It is quite possible to observe these principles at work in the mind of even the youngest infant, when, for example a young child becomes aware of the difference between his own mother and the strange examiner doing a test; and even without speech he can demonstrate his awareness of the difference! Later he discovers relationships between many objects (fundaments) in his surroundings. He realises relationships of size — that one brick is bigger than another. He does not at first know the verbal meaning of the adjective "big". He "becomes aware" or learns to recognise, the differences within his limited experience, of taste, touch, sight and sound, from

1 See Bibliography, p. 176.

a very early age. This process is continuous throughout infancy and indeed throughout life.

By the third year the child becomes aware of the difference in size between a penny and a shilling, but has at first no idea of any difference in value of the two coins. Later on (in the Vth year) he learns to *name* the most familiar coins correctly, and get some idea of their relative values.

The child also acquires a knowledge of sequences, and presently he is learning to count and so gradually grasps the numerical sequence, which precedes and underlies arithmetical comprehension, and mathematical subjects generally. This sequence is almost entirely built up of relationships between numbers or values, and to use these ideas is constantly to use "correlate eduction". At an early stage the young child becomes aware, through trial and error, of the number of fingers he has on each hand, the very elementary basis of the decimal system! Soon he gives evidence of understanding a high tower of little cubes, and can distinguish it from a "low" one. He recognises that one line is longer than another. He is hampered in his practical thinking by his need to learn the terminology, but the *ideas* behind the terminology are not purely verbal, but have a practical bearing and multiply as thought develops. Later, when he knows the "names" that clothe the ideas he can *communicate* these ideas to others.

So, in Scale F, beginning at the third year, we explore the stage a child has reached in his attempts to comprehend his environment, by looking at the things around him (through play with small toys and other objects) comparing, contrasting, placing them in an orderly manner, first by actual handling of objects, by testing their qualities with eyes, ears and lips, and by coming to conclusions about them.

Then such practical matters, over the space of several years, as how to read the clock face and tell the time, involve awareness of the separate functions of the two hands of the clock and their changing spatial and temporal relationships with one another. It requires considerable effort on the part of a little child to master this very practical problem.

Perhaps enough has been said at this stage to explain why these particular tests have been gathered together in this way in a separate scale. Individual differences in this scale are as great as in any of the other five scales.

The accompanying percentage table (Table XII) begins with the

PRACTICAL REASONING   SCALE F

TABLE XII

From Two to Eight Years

Note: The tests of this Scale, Practical Reasoning, begin with Year III, although a few children in Year II can pass some of the items.

Items:	Years: No.	I N=427	II 436	III 327	IV 274	V 285	VI 223	VII 211	VIII 77	Total N 2260
										Passing each item
Year III										
Repeats one digit: 8; 2; 7	III 1	0	4.4	63.6	98.2	100	100	100	100	1292
Knows 'penny' or 'money'	III 2	0	6.1	51.9	92.3	100	100	100	100	1245
Repeats two digits: 16; 53; 94	III 3	0	2.3	51.4	90.5	98.9	100	99.5	100	1218
Compares 2 insets for size	III 4	0	1.8	37.0	85.8	97.5	100	100	100	1153
Repeats three digits: 982; 475; 136	III 5	0	1.1	26.3	74.4	91.9	99.1	98.6	98.7	1062
Knows 'big' and 'little'	III 6	0	.2	18.3	74.4	95.1	96.9	99.0	98.7	1037
Year IV										
Compares 2 towers: 5; 3	IV 1		.5	26.6	68.6	87.7	97.3	99.0	100	1030
Compares for length (2 lines)	IV 2		.5	15.6	67.5	93.3	97.3	98.1	98.7	1004
Preliminary counting to 4 plus	IV 3		.2	9.2	38.3	81.7	97.8	98.6	100	872
Counts 4 bricks	IV 4		0	3.9	25.9	70.9	92.8	97.6	100	776
Repeats 4 digits	IV 5		.2	6.4	31.0	65.6	87.0	88.6	93.5	747
Compares 2 weights	IV 6		0	9.2	29.6	58.2	77.6	83.9	92.2	698
Year V										
Names 2 coins	V 1		0	4.3	16.1	50.9	87.4	93.4	100	672
Can count 10 bricks	V 2		0	.9	9.9	44.6	82.5	92.4	100	613
Knows morning and afternoon	V 3		0	2.7	21.9	46.7	72.6	82.9	92.2	610
Names 3 coins	V 4		0	1.5	6.2	31.9	73.5	88.4	96.1	537
'Which goes faster'?	V 5		0	3.4	13.5	46.7	60.1	72.5	84.5	533
Can count 15 bricks	V 6		0	0	3.6	21.4	61.9	86.2	100	468

TABLE XII PRACTICAL REASONING SCALE F — continued

Items:	Years: No.	I N=427	II 436	III 327	IV 274	V 285	VI 223	VII 211	VIII 77	Total N 2260
										Passing each item
Year VI										
Knows number of fingers, each hand	VI 1		0	0	1.8	17.9	58.7	84.8	98.7	442
Names 4 coins	VI 2		0	0	2.9	21.1	58.3	80.6	93.5	440
Names 5 coins	VI 3		0	0	.4	13.0	43.5	77.3	85.7	364
Repeats 5 digits	VI 4		0	.3	6.9	24.6	39.5	58.8	75.3	360
Knows 10 fingers (5 plus 5)	VI 5		0	0	0	9.8	37.2	82.9	94.8	359
Knows 'high' and 'low'	VI 6		0	.9	10.6	30.2	37.7	48.8	45.5	346
Year VII										
Counts to 30	VII 1			0	.4	7.0	38.1	77.3	90.9	339
Knows 'right' and 'left' (8 plus)	VII 2			.6	2.9	22.8	29.6	51.2	64.9	299
Can count backwards from '10'	VII 3			0	0	3.5	26.0	71.1	87.0	285
Can say the days of the week	VII 4			0	1.4	8.4	28.3	55.4	80.5	270
Tells the time, hours only	VII 5			0	.7	9.5	24.2	57.8	68.8	258
Knows 'long' and 'short'	VII 6			0	3.6	19.3	21.5	37.0	45.5	226
Year VIII										
Days of week, questions all correct	VIII 1				.4	5.6	17.0	44.5	77.9	209
Names 6 coins	VIII 2				0	2.8	16.1	47.9	72.7	201
Says three digits backwards	VIII 3				0	3.2	14.8	44.1	75.3	193
Knows 'heavy' and 'light'	VIII 4				0	2.1	11.2	39.3	58.4	159
Can count backwards from '20'	VIII 5				0	0	4.5	36.0	66.2	137
Names 7 coins	VIII 6				0	.7	5.8	31.8	57.1	126
Year IX										
Tells the time, half-hours	IX 1					.4	4.5	26.1	39.0	96
Tells the time, quarter-hours	IX 2					.4	1.3	11.8	24.7	48

Year VI | Year VII | Year VIII | Year IX

top of the second year where a small number of babies were successful at one or more items of this scale (Year III) and continues like the other scales up to the end of the eighth year and into the ninth.

In this section we have glanced very briefly at each of the six sub-scales, as it were, as separate measuring rods. In the next Chapter we shall deal with the six-scale test as a whole, and show the inter-related sequences in association with one another.

Before closing this Chapter we would like to draw the attention to the long column of figures on the right-hand side of each of the percentage tables: Tables VII to XII. These figures represent the total numbers of children credited with each item throughout the length of the scales. In other words, they represent the number of children who passed the particular item under test, or were credited with it because it belonged to the basic section of the scale in each case; just as when scoring an individual test result, mental age credits are given for those earlier years of the test, that it is un-necessary to take. It was thought interesting thus to arrive at the total number of credits for each test item, which was easily achieved from the charts. A further line on the accuracy of the work, and in particular on the "equality of difficulty" of the scales, can therefore be obtained by totalling these columns, and then dividing the totals by 2,260 to get the *average* number of items credited to each child in each of these six sub-scales. In the following brief table these results are presented.

TABLE XIII

TOTAL ITEMS CREDITED IN EACH SCALE
WITH AVERAGES

Total items credited		*Average number passed*
Scale A	108,264	......	47.90
Scale B	107,941	......	47.75
Scale C	107,907	......	47.75
Scale D	108,436	......	47.98
Scale E	107,664	......	47.64
Scale F	107,898	......	47.74

Thus approximately an average of 48 items were credited to each child, in each scale, which suggests a high degree of equality of difficulty between the six sub-scales, in spite of the manifest differences in the subject matter of the tests.

This high degree of equality between the six sub-scales was also shown at the end of Chapter V, Table VI, where the total annual quotients in each scale were given and also the total quotients in each annual sample. The smaller sample of children in the eighth year (77) gave somewhat lower results, this was due also to the inevitable ceiling effect at the top of the scales.

This equality of difficulty in the sub-scales will also be exemplified in the next Chapter (Chapter VII) when we deal with the frequency distributions.

The equality of the sub-scales is stressed throughout this book in several ways, as it is upon this fact of reasonable equality at all levels between the six scales, that the whole thesis of this book rests. This thesis is that only through demonstrable equality between the scales, can we arrive at "Differential Diagnosis of Mental Status".

The significance of this thesis will be further exemplified when we examine the results of testing both normal and handicapped children, and look at the resulting profiles, in Chapters VIII and IX.

CHAPTER VII

FREQUENCY DISTRIBUTIONS AND CORRELATIONS

IN the last chapter we showed the six scales of the total examination in their entirety and presented the percentage tables resulting from the testing of 2,260 children.

It now becomes important to show the effect of transmuting the test results into M.A.'s[1] and thence into Quotients, which were worked up by the usual formula used for mental tests:

$$\text{G.Q.} = \frac{\text{M.A.} \times 100}{\text{C.A.}}$$

Frequency Distributions and Standard Deviations can now be looked at for all the six sub-scales. These are summarised below, see Table XIV, and the frequency distributions are shown in Figures I to VII.

TABLE XIV

TABLE OF TOTAL TEST RESULTS

Quotients and Standard Deviations of the Sub-scales

Scale	Quotient	Sigma	N.
A. Locomotor Development	100.41	16.32	2,260
B. Personal-Social Development	100.26	16.20	2,260
C. Hearing and Speech	99.78	17.75	2,260
D. Hand and Eye Co-ordination	100.46	15.58	2,260
E. Performance Tests	99.87	17.21	2,260
F. Practical Reasoning	99.79	17.43	1,544*
Total Scale	100.18	12.76	2,260

* Note re Scale F. A special note is required here to remind the reader that Scale F. begins at the third year, and that very few babies below two years of age can do these F. Scale tests. Nonetheless the total number of children under examination was 2,260, in all the other 5 scales and in the total scale.

[1] M.A.—Mental Age.   C.A.—Actual or Chronological Age.
    G.Q.—General Intelligence Quotient.

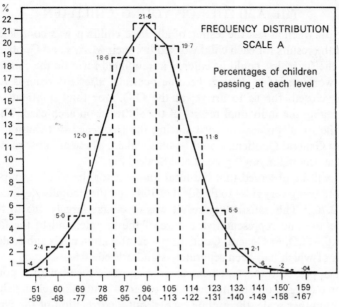

FIG. 1   LOCOMOTOR DEVELOPMENT   A.Q.'s
Years I to VIII   N = 2260   A.Q. = 100·41   S.D. 16·32

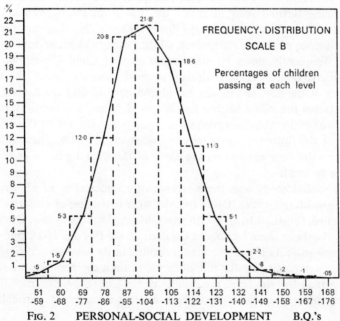

FIG. 2   PERSONAL-SOCIAL DEVELOPMENT   B.Q.'s
Years I to VIII   N = 2260   B.Q. = 100·26   S.D. 16·20

Now when at last the testing of all these children was completed, and the results for each child worked up, their M.A.'s and Quotients for the six scales, could be entered in tabulated form on the cards of the working index. It then became possible, after the records had been closed, for us to arrive, at the G.Q.'s or total quotients by averaging the individual results of the six tests, on each card. Then by the usual process of card sorting the frequency distribution of these General Quotients could be undertaken. These are now shown in the accompanying figure, Total Scales, Fig. 7.

It will be observed that the total quotient for the whole group is 100.18 being very close to the ideal of 100 (and the standard deviation is 12.76).[1] This satisfactory result was of course largely due to the large size and representative nature of the sample, and to the fact that the G.Q. or General Quotient is a combination of six sub-scales, each of which had been separately standardised.

It appeared important next to compare this result with a good sample of tests on another scale. In order to study this relationship with another scale, the author carried out a correlation of the New Scale with the Terman-Merrill tests that had been done on some of our children. There had been no particular selection of children for Terman-Merrill testing arranged for, but from the beginning the examiners had been asked to do this extra test as an additional piece of evidence whenever convenient, whilst testing a child, and this was also frequently done by the author at the Child Development Research Centre. Having already in most cases completed the six scales of the new test it was not always easy to find the necessary additional time for a further test in school. When a Terman-Merrill test *was* undertaken however, it was usually carried out on the same day as the fuller test, or within one week of that date. These extra test results were entered on the cards of the working index as they came to hand.

A special study was therefore recently undertaken of all these Terman-Merrill tests. It was found that a scattering of children in the third, fourth, fifth and sixth years, had had this extra test. Others had also been done on school children above this age level, but as the new scale itself was reaching its ceiling in the seventh and eighth years, it was felt best for this purpose, to limit the material for the *correlation* to tests from the middle of the age range, i.e. from the years three to six inclusive. There was no selection of particular

[1] See also the standard deviation of the 604 babies tested for the earlier research: "The Abilities of Babies", p. 73, where the S.D. is 12.12.

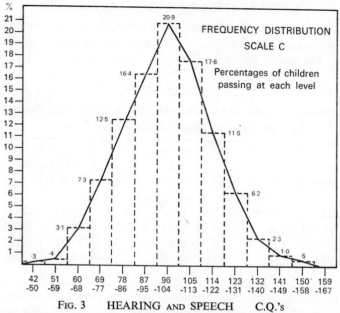

FIG. 3   HEARING AND SPEECH   C.Q.'s
Years I to VIII   N = 2260   C.Q. = 99·78   S.D. 17·75

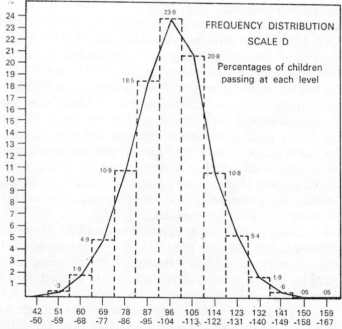

FIG. 4   HAND AND EYE CO-ORDINATION   D.Q.'s
Years I to VIII   N = 2260   D.Q. 100·46   S.D. 15·58

children or groups of children. These correlations were carried out on *all* the tests from children of these ages who had been given both tests. The results are shown below in Table XV.

TABLE XV

Correlation Results between the Six-Scale Test (General Quotients) and the Terman-Merrill Tests (I.Q.s). Form L.

Year	N	G.Q.	I.Q. Form L	Sigma G.Q.	Sigma Form L	r
III	97	101.92	106.87	11.79	15.48	.7935
IV	130	99.45	106.64	12.64	16.12	.8026
V	140	99.63	104.73	12.98	17.72	.8143
VI	157	100.15	102.77	11.11	13.85	.7970

It will be seen that the correlations with the Terman-Merrill Scale are quite high, and suggest a substantial Common Factor between the two tests in spite of considerable difference in subject matter of the actual tests included.

It is pertinent to note that the somewhat high Terman-Merrill, Form L. I.Q.'s shown in this table are closely similar to those quoted on page 35 of "Measuring Intelligence", Terman and Merrill, 1935 edition which range for these same ages from 101 to 109!

The next step was to get some idea of the inter-relationship between the separate Scales of the Griffiths Test itself. To learn more about this, correlations had been carried out, on sections of the range earlier in the work, and these correlations had been reassuring. When therefore, all the data had been collected and certain studies of the equality of difficulty had been completed for the total project, it became possible to obtain more complete results by carrying out correlations, on certain definite sections of the range, correlating the quotients of each scale with the total G.Q.

The fifth year was the best to select for this purpose. The number of children in this fifth year being 285, gave a reasonable size for correlation purposes, and also it lies right in the middle of the age range of the total samples of older children (3 to 8 years). Also the problem of the ceiling effect found at the top of the range, in the 7th and 8th years was avoided; and the very young children who could not do the sixth scale were not involved. These correlations

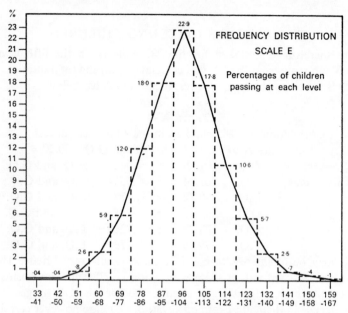

Fig. 5   PERFORMANCE TESTS

Years I to VIII   N = 2260   E.Q. 99·87   S.D. 17·21

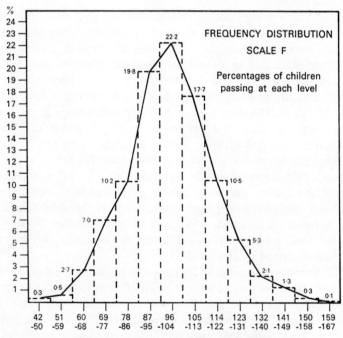

Fig. 6   PRACTICAL REASONING

Years II to VIII   N = 1544   F.Q. 99·79   S.D. 17·43

71

were therefore undertaken for the 285 children in the fifth year. Each sub-scale from A to F was correlated with the total quotients, G.Q.'s, of these children. The results are tabulated below.

TABLE XVI

Correlations on 285 children in their fifth year at test,
Sub-scales A to F and G.Q.   Total G.Q. 100.20

Quotients of	A.Q.	101.38	r = .6419	A.Q. and G.Q.
Sub-scales	B.Q.	101.04	r = .6537	B.Q. and G.Q.
	C.Q.	99.72	r = .7776	C.Q. and G.Q.
	D.Q.	99.96	r = .7551	D.Q. and G.Q.
	E.Q.	100.08	r = .7265	E.Q. and G.Q.
	F.Q.	99.36	r = .7793	F.Q. and G.Q.

It may be of interest to consider these results very briefly. The first obvious fact is that these correlation co-efficients are positive and quite high, suggesting a common factor of "G" or general intelligence in them all. From observation there are however certain interesting differences in the degree of saturation with "G" of the separate Scales.

Scale A measuring Locomotor Development, as it does, a certain amount of physical activity is involved, requiring a degree of normal physical strength compatible with the ages of the children, all in their fifth year. Also skill in movement, sometimes speed of movement, rhythm and poise are needed. Interesting problems here arise, as a simple measure of locomotor development even at this early age, may be not unrelated to a possible *future* competence in physical movement, associated with skills in various branches of sport, physical training and athletics. So that, although we may be measuring physical normality and skill in movement (as far as a single avenue of development can be isolated from the rest) nonetheless factors of concentration on a task or persistence in an activity, as well as normal physical strength and maturity are involved. There is also a factor of conation, what used to be called the 'W' factor present here, relating to an emotional determination or will to succeed, described by Dr. Webb.[1]

The most important reason for including a Locomotor Scale is due however, from the present writer's point of view, to a desire to have opportunity to observe and locate where necessary any slight or more serious physical weakness or disability. The fact that other scales in these sequences, produce higher correlation co-efficients

[1] Webb. British Journal of Psychology. Mon. Supp. 1915, No. III.

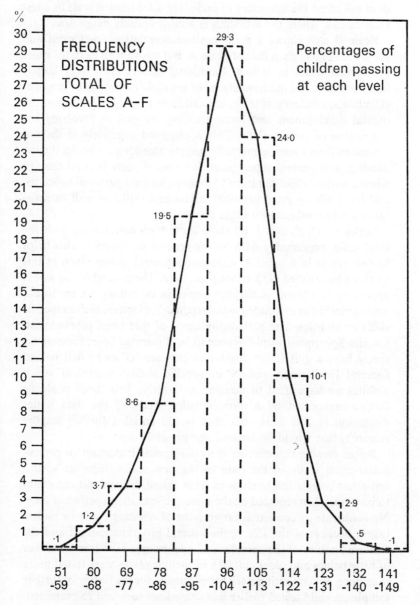

FIG. 7 TOTAL OF SCALES A–F   GENERAL QUOTIENTS   G.Q.'s
All VIII Year   N = 2260   G.Q. = 100·18   S.D. 12·76

73

does not affect the ligitimacy of including a locomotor scale in a test such as this, where the intention is almost entirely diagnostic.

Scale B also shows a good positive correlation co-efficient and somewhat higher than that of Scale A, but not so high as in the more intellectual scales to follow. Emotional factors enter very largely into this scale, and the competence of the child in matters of personal cleanliness, efficiency at table, etc., all have a relationship to normal mental development and home training, as well as involving the acquisition of certain skills. This is observed negatively in the sad condition found among mentally defective children, who need care, nursing, and general supervision, for several years beyond the age when a normal child can learn to manage his own personal concerns, and has built up good personal habits and skills, as well as satisfactory relationships with other people.

Scales C, D, E, and F all show quite high correlations with the total scale, presumably with 'G' or general intelligence. This helps to confirm us in a belief in a common general factor which in this work we have called G.Q. or total quotient. The general factor would appear to be present in varying degree in everything we try to do, but intermixed or associated with certain other factors, such as specific skills or abilities. The philosophy again of that great psychologist, Charles Spearman[1] would appear to be illustrated here; for here we surely have a quite clear distinction between 'G' as he first named General Intelligence, and 'S' or specific ability, several of which abilities we have tried to measure separately. This thesis could be further elaborated by a more detailed study of the data under discussion in this work, but that would entail a further lengthy research, that would go beyond our present purposes.

Before closing this chapter it would appear important to present a test-retest study of the data of the new scales, together with a test-retest correlation to show to what extent the new test can claim to be valid, when repeated on the same subjects after a period of time. No deliberate or consistent programme of retesting could be undertaken, because of the size of the general programme itself and the scattered nature of the samples and age groups. However a number of little babies and older children in various places were tested more than once. When visiting a school or nursery for the testing of further samples, a child tested earlier was sometimes seen and re-examined. A correlation of a small sample of children tested twice was done in

1 See "The Abilities of Man", by C. Spearman, Mc.Millan, 1927, Chapter XI: The Universality of "G".

connection with the earlier work and will be found in "The Abilities of Babies". (N=60)[1] r= ·87. In the present study a total of 270 second tests were collected.

In the following tables are shown the age range of the children who were retested, and the distance in time between the tests year by year. Finally we can quote the very satisfactory test-retest correlation of these 270 re-tests, r=.774748, see Table XVI. Please also see Table XVII.

Notes on the Test-retest Correlation, distance between tests

TABLE XVII

Year of Age at First Test	N	Length of Time Between Tests
Year I	57	3 to 31 months
Year II	52	3 to 62 months
Year III	42	6 to 34 months
Year IV	45	6 to 40 months
Year V	40	6 to 32 months
Year VI	21	6 to 14 months
Year VII	13	6 to 14 months

Total Retested N = 270

Correlation Co-efficient r = .774748

It will be noted that the distances between test and retest range from 3 months to 62 months.

It is usual of course for the correlation to decrease as the distance in time between test and restest increases. In view also of the young ages of most of the children this correlation of .77 on the total retests would appear to be very satisfactory, as a measure of reliability.

[1] See "The Abilities of Babies", p. 76.

CHAPTER VIII

PROFILES OF YOUNG CHILDREN
A DEVELOPMENTAL STUDY OF INDIVIDUAL DIFFERENCES

As will be realised by those who have read the previous chapters of this book, the main thesis we have tried to develop throughout, is that concerning the equality of difficulty between the several scales of the new test.

Only if the averages and standard deviations of the several sub-scales can be demonstrated to be very closely similar, can we say categorically that a child has failed or succeeded more at one sequence than he has at another. The pattern of learning, and the resulting responses of the children, change from child to child under examination, and from time to time with the same child, as he catches up on one avenue of learning, or drops behind on another. Periodic testing of the same child, can show these effects. The child who shows a consistently low result for example, on Scale C, compared with the rest of his own performance, may possibly be a deaf child, or be suffering from a degree of hearing loss. One who fails consistently on Scales A and D, Locomotor Development and Hand and Eye Co-ordination, but does better on other scales, is almost certainly physically defective, or possibly suffering from a degree of muscular weakness. If this child does very much better on the other sub-scales this impression is increased. The child who fails specifically on Scale B is likely to be an unhappy or maladjusted child. In all such cases further investigation of the child's mental or physical state should be undertaken by the appropriate medical authorities.

In this chapter we shall show profiles of normal and near-normal children. In the next chapter, Chapter IX, we shall turn to a study of some of those sadder cases where the child is suffering from a definite degree of defect or disability, or from impaired health.

The profile therefore in the right hands becomes a truly diagnostic instrument, in that it shows in a preliminary and provisional way where a weakness or difficulty lies or is likely to lie.

Profiles of babies under two years of age were shown in the earlier volume,[1] Chapters VII and VIII. There, the five scale test was used. In the present volume we are able to use the six scales to complete the profile.

Let us now turn to an examination of some of these profiles. In the accompanying Figure 9, cases numbered 1, 2, and 3, show the profiles of three children of average ability, with total quotients a little below or above 100, but showing sometimes (see Case 1) quite large differences between the several sub-scales that make up the total examination.

Case 1, a girl of about $3\frac{1}{2}$ years of age, gets an average result on Scale A, indicating that she is able to walk, run, climb stairs, etc., at about her own chronological age level. Scale B shows her to be doing very well on the social side, able to dress herself, fasten her own shoes, and help nicely in the home, etc. Speech too is very satisfactory, but on the more practical side, Scales D and F she does not do so well. (Scale F only begins at year III).

Case 2 is a boy of just average ability, just four years old, with some slight weakness of musculature making him slow for his general level on Scales A and D. Belonging to a superior family he is getting suitable help and encouragement and is improving physically, as well as learning at a normal rate. At present he tests as a normal average child. Later as he begins formal education, all round improvement may be looked for.

Case 3. Here is the profile of a lovely little girl, just four years of age. She tested at average ability, not yet doing much with Scale F, but showing satisfactory results on all the other scales. Her relationship with other people is very good, and speech is developing nicely, with a good vocabulary for her age, and she is using sentences well.

Case 4. (See Fig. 9). This is the profile of an average boy, five years of age, with good Locomotor Development, active physically, and developing normally in all directions, but with a higher than average level on Scale A.

Case 5. This profile presents a varied and unusual picture. It is the profile of a small girl with a high verbal ability and shows very good social development, but she does not do so well at practical or performance tests, where she shows only average or below average results.

Case 6. This is a somewhat similar result to that of No. 5. This boy has, however, for his age great physical energy, and is somewhat

[1] See "The Abilities of Babies", pp. 81 to 99.

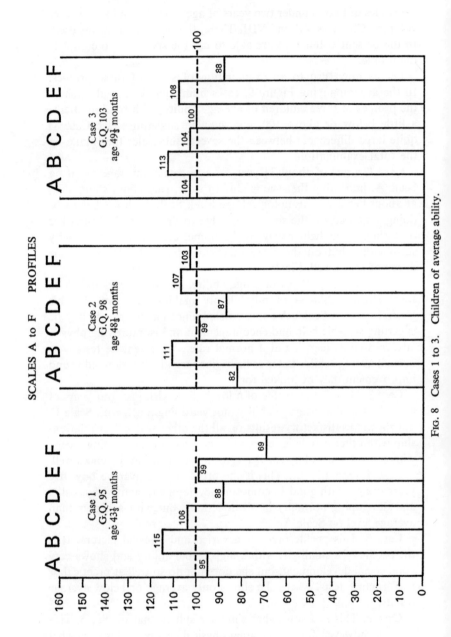

SCALES A to F   PROFILES

Case 1
G.Q. 95
age 43⅓ months

Case 2
G.Q. 98
age 48⅓ months

Case 3
G.Q. 103
age 49⅓ months

FIG. 8   Cases 1 to 3.   Children of average ability.

78

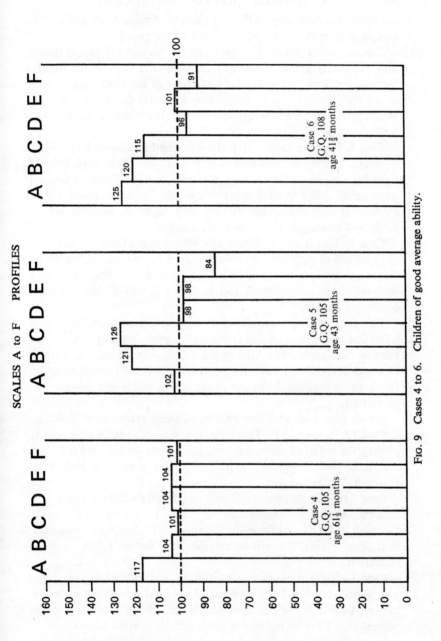

SCALES A to F PROFILES

Case 4
G.Q. 105
age 61⅓ months

Case 5
G.Q. 105
age 43 months

Case 6
G.Q. 108
age 41⅔ months

FIG. 9 Cases 4 to 6. Children of good average ability.

excitable. He does very well at $3\frac{1}{2}$ years on Scales A, B, and C, but not so well on the more practical side of the profile.

Case 7. (See Fig 10). This boy, tall for his age ($3\frac{1}{2}$ years) strong and physically active, he scores an unusually high result on the Locomotor Scale, where he did some tests of the sixth year, as well as all the locomotor tests below that level. He did not do so outstandingly well in other directions, but the total result (112) is well above the average.

Case 8. Here we have a very attractive and intelligent little girl of $5\frac{1}{4}$ years. Her speech was remarkably good, she could actually *read* fluently, and was able to read a simple but previously unknown passage of prose from a story book. She shows a result above average at everything, and is very well adjusted, meeting people easily and coming to the testing room alone.

Case 9. This is an intelligent boy with a remarkable profile. The G.Q. of 128 though high for this test, does not do him justice, as he was passing tests of the eighth year in several scales and could probably have gone further still in Scales E and F, had the tests continued further.

This Case 9 is an example of the problem created by the ceiling effect due to the tests ending at the eighth year. Actually two further tests in each scale are added at the ninth year. Nonetheless these clever children, few in number, do lose a possible further point or two because they reach the top of the scales, and might conceivably go further.

Let us now look at a few profiles of some rather slow children.

Case 10. (See Fig. 11). This little boy, himself only $2\frac{1}{2}$ years old is already the eldest of three children. His results on tests are low, but are fairly even, suggesting a generally slow mental development, at about 75% of normal.

Case 11. This is another slowly developing child, a girl of 37 months. All her test results are at a low level indicating a total Quotient of 66. Unless dramatic improvement takes place during the next year or two, she will be suitable only for an E.S.N. type of education.

Case 12. Here is another slow child, a boy nearly five years old, who shows a general Quotient of 61. He did somewhat better at performance tests for his level, but his results on other sub-scales suggest that he is by no means ready yet for normal school.

Let us finalise this chapter on a more hopeful note by showing the profiles of three of the most intelligent children in the whole

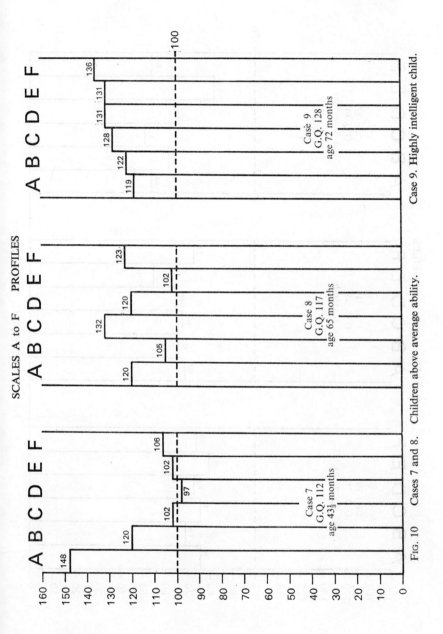

SCALES A to F   PROFILES

Case 7
G.Q. 112
age 43½ months

Case 8
G.Q. 117
age 65 months

Case 9
G.Q. 128
age 72 months

Fig. 10   Cases 7 and 8.   Children above average ability.

Case 9.   Highly intelligent child.

81

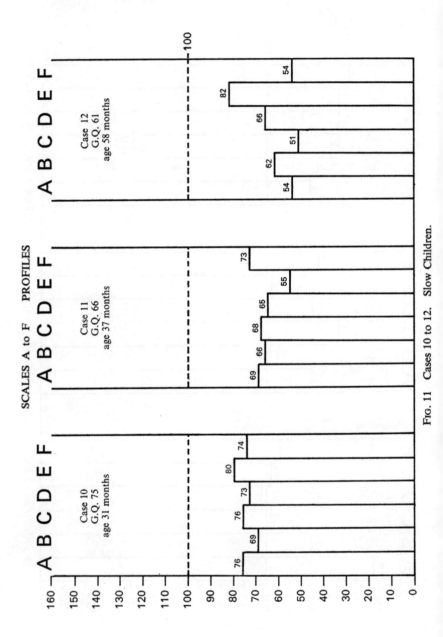

SCALES A to F   PROFILES

Case 10
G.Q. 75
age 31 months

Case 11
G.Q. 66
age 37 months

Case 12
G.Q. 61
age 58 months

Fig. 11   Cases 10 to 12.   Slow Children.

82

sample of 2,260 children. These are shown below, Cases 13 to 15. All three have quotients the same as one another, i.e. 134. (See Fig. 12), but their abilities differ considerably from one another, as will be seen by a comparison of their quotients on the separate scales.

These three very bright children are one boy and two girls. They belong to the top eight of the whole of this large sample. Although all three have the same total Quotient, or G.Q., it will be seen that the shapes of these profiles differ widely from one another. **Case 13** does best at speech and at practical reasoning, the two most intellectual of the scales. **Case 14** does best at Scale A (physical activity) and at Scale C, verbal ability, while **Case 15** does outstandingly well at Scale E, performance tests, suggesting good comprehension of space and form relations. All these three are very clever children. To achieve a G.Q. of 140 on these scales would probably be a maximum. This was achieved by one child only in the whole group.

These very brief notes about each of these cases, most of them normal boys and girls between 3 and 6 years of age, may serve to provide a first preliminary glance at the nature of the assessment that can be obtained by this profile technique. Certainly the method uncovers the handicaps where they exist, and shows the effects they are having or are likely to have on the child's progress towards the years when education in its widest sense becomes important.

It also does justice to the positive side, giving the young child scope to demonstrate what skills he possesses. It would seem by no means too soon to carry out such a test as this on any child whose educational future is in doubt, or one who has a difficult health problem, or social problem, due sometimes to frequent changes of home background in infancy and early childhood.

In general the new technique can throw significant light on the problems of Child Development, Child Health, and Education. The allocation of young children to nurseries, infant schools, E.S.N. schools, or to the normal schools are matters of such great urgency and importance, that a thorough assessment of every child in the pre-school period would seem to be not merely advisable, but almost obligatory. At least an assessment of this kind is a necessity where there is a problem.

In the next chapter we shall look at profiles taken in the wider context of hospital, and health and welfare centre, where the diagnostic significance of the profile can be shown more clearly.

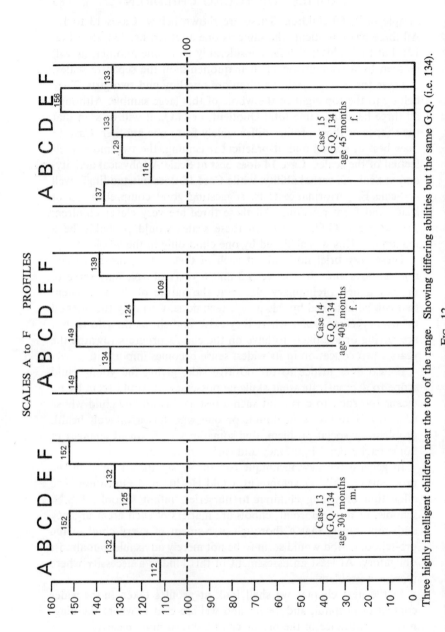

Three highly intelligent children near the top of the range. Showing differing abilities but the same G.Q. (i.e. 134).

Fig. 12

CHAPTER IX

PROFILES OF HANDICAPPED CHILDREN

In this section we must give our attention to that group of children, for the fuller understanding of whom all this work has been undertaken. Throughout a long life of work among children the writer has met with many little ones suffering from disabilities, that not only caused suffering to the children themselves, but unhappiness to the parents, and other members of the family. Such disabilities also precluded in many cases, a normal education. The parents also suffered in their day by day association with these problems, bravely going on with the routine of living, while they gradually came to realise that the little handicapped one might be a problem always.

The old idea that children grow out of handicaps, or will be better later on, has been so frequently and pathetically falsified by events, that it is completely discredited now. What is needed is early investigation of the problem and a close collaboration by all concerned in a joint or comprehensive programme of help for the handicapped child and his parents. Thus the paediatrician may call on colleagues specialising in one department or another of Child Health. A speech case is sent to an audiologist for investigation of possible hearing loss, later the patient may go to a speech surgeon, and thence to a speech therapist, and so on with other conditions. That wonderfully versatile person, the social worker can be useful all along the line. Many people deal with the same cases at different times, and each sees the problem from the point of view of his own speciality or special function. A great deal is being achieved, in fact many so-called modern miracles are taking place around us in all branches of medicine, surgery, child health and education both normal and special. Deaf babies can be given a hearing aid at a surprisingly early age. Congenital cataracts can sometimes be removed and the child helped to make use of his vision, as he gradually adjusts to the new sensations of sight that he experiences.

The cerebral palsied child, according to the nature and degree of his handicaps, can be educated, and helped by physical treatment as well as by mechanical aids, to learn to move about in his world, and accept some degree of education. He will be able in due course to make contact with other children in a group, as for example at school, or in a nursery.

Little mongol children are now-a-days much better understood. The genetic aspect of their problem makes the condition intractable, but much research is going on. A small percentage of these children can accept a degree of education in E.S.N. schools or in special groups. The majority can have a training, according to their capacity to respond, in occupation centres. Some are too retarded even for this degree of help, and must remain at home, or in hospital, or in special care units, where they can develop slowly, varying in their capacity to mature, but rarely able to take anything approaching a normal place in life.

Thalidomide children are usually normal in intelligence. Their difficulties are mainly physical, due to the lack of one or more limbs, for which conditions appliances are being invented, and constantly improved, to help the clever thalidomide child to take an active part in life. It is to be hoped that no more of this condition will be encountered, as the cause is now known.

Some very interesting work has been done over the past two or three decades, in the biochemical field, with dietary treatment of phenylketonuria, and other related conditions; and fullow-up studies of backwardness resulting from this condition, show a marked improvement in mental capacity in a proportion of cases.

It would fill a much larger volume than the present one merely to describe even briefly those branches of medicine and social work and education that are involved in attempts to mitigate the problems of the handicapped.

What relevance has all this to the theme of this book? In the past many handicapped children have grown up in families, who realised that there was something unusual or definitely wrong, in one of their children. In many cases apparently little could be done either to diagnose the condition or help to correct it. To-day we realise that children do not grow out of these disabilities, and from the point of view of the psychologist, the first thing to do would appear to be, to see such children very much earlier than has been customary, and study their reactions and abilities in relation to the known normal trends. Hence it would appear that the sooner a problem is brought to light and investigated the better. Earlier studies of mental capacity were largely limited to adults and school children. To-day we descend

to the very beginning of life, and carry out our child study pro-
grammes from the earliest weeks and months.

The necessity to come to a position where we can compare one
child with another, or a backward child with his own age-group,
and do this with a high degree of accuracy, is the first step towards
getting help, whenever possible, for that child. We need to discover
and assess the nature of the problem in two separate ways, by
asking two questions: (1) How retarded is this child? (2) In what
specific direction is he failing? The first question leads to an understanding, not only of the child's total pottential, but also his relation
ship to his own age group. The second question asks in what particular directions, if any, does he fail? We need the basic information
that will enlighten us as to his problem, and then we may be in a
position to decide what can be done to help him, and to advise his
parents.

Only after many years of experience of Mental Testing, did the
realisation come forcibly to the writer, that tests must be carried
down below the usual ages for mental testing, and must be designed
for, and used with, both normal and handicapped children from a
very early age. Only thus could we discover the specific effects of
handicaps on the *learning* process.

Gesell and Buhler and other makers of tests for young children
mainly in America, had classified their test items in several ways.
Locomotor activity, and handwork, were separated from social and
verbal responses. No attempt was made to allocate mental ages
separately for different areas of development, or arrive at separate
quotients. We have called these separate areas "Avenues of Learning"
and have standardised these separately as was explained in earlier
chapters of this book, into six separate scales. From the point of
view of the present writer, the whole process of mental growth and
development is largely a question of learning capacity, and "G" or
general intelligence.

Thus a particular brain damaged child finds difficulty in *learning*
to walk. A deaf child is obstructed from *learning* to speak, because
he does not hear the sounds that give the clue to the meaning of
spoken language. Similarly a blind child knows by touch without
sight, only gradually can he learn to understand "space and form
relations", and is therefore backward in manipulation of toys and
other materials.

These new scales therefore are a logical development of much that
has gone before in mental testing experiments and psychological

theories, as well as educational practices. To separate the essential avenues of learning from one another in separate scales enables the investigator to evaluate each major sequence apart from the rest. At the same time all these several means of measuring the avenues of learning must surely be equal in difficulty at each age level, if we are to be in a position to state quite definitely, that a child has done better on examination, at one such avenue than he has at another.

Thus emerges the six-scale test, which not only gives us a new scale for the study of mental development in general, in infancy and early childhood, but it gives us also a truly diagnostic technique that can throw light upon the problems of young handicapped children.

These scales can therefore provide the *first step* in diagnosis. Their function is not to say categorically "this child is deaf", but to show that on the six scale test the child fails on Scale C, and does less well than his total capacity would suggest, on Scale B (the personal-social scale) but does much better on Scale A (learning to walk) and on Scales D and E (because he can see and handle toys and test materials). Such a child therefore is not fundamentally a backward or imbecile child, but may conceivably be suffering from hearing loss.

The function of these Scales therefore is not to say categorically what the reason may be for a child's slowness on Scales A and D for example. The profile itself will demonstrate this slowness clearly. It is for the paediatrician or other specialist, to discover the *reason* for this failure. The slowness in these two scales may be patent, but the fact that he does better on the other four scales will emphasise the point, and show the limited effect of the retardation, and show that this is not a case of all-round mental deficiency however low these two results may be, but one that might conceivably respond to treatment.

Perhaps sufficient has been said at this point, to indicate the function of these tests. Let us then conclude this chapter and Part II by a brief study of a few cases of handicapped children known and tested by the writer on the completed scales.

Cases 1 to 15 were briefly described in Chapter VIII.

CASE STUDIES OF HANDICAPPED CHILDREN

We will begin this section with three cases of severely retarded children. (See the accompanying profiles, Fig. 13).

Case 16. This little boy aged $40\frac{1}{2}$ months, that is 3 years and $4\frac{1}{2}$ months old, has a mental age of $22\frac{1}{2}$ months. That provides a total general intelligence quotient (G.Q.) of 56.

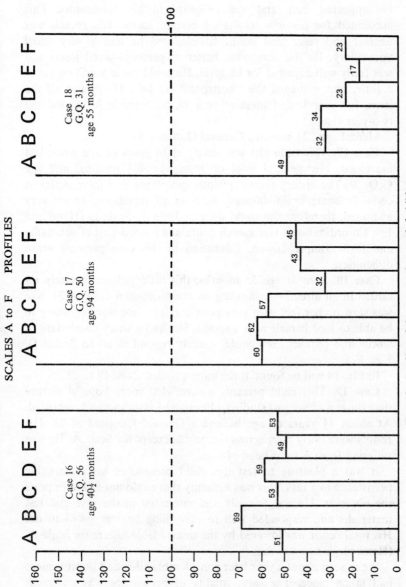

Fig. 13 Profiles of three severely retarded children.

SCALES A to F PROFILES

Case 16
G.Q. 56
age 40½ months

Case 17
G.Q. 50
age 94 months

Case 18
G.Q. 31
age 55 months

At test he showed himself to be an attractive but very slow child. He appeared frail, and was awkward in his movements. This accounted for his low results on certain scales. His speech was unclear and resembled infant babble, and he had a very small vocabulary. He did somewhat better at personal-social items and was fairly well adjusted for his level. He could use a pencil on paper a little, and managed the "horizontal stroke". He passed all the items for year I, and most of year II, but very little beyond the two-year level.

Mental age 22½ months, General Quotient 56.

Case 17. This little girl was nearly eight years of age when last examined. Her general level on tests was 46½ months, and her G.Q. 50. The history shows epileptic symptoms, and there is almost certainly some brain damage. Slow in all directions, hands very awkward, therefore she could do very little on Scale D (Hand and Eye Co-ordination). Her speech contained a good deal of echolalia, and little comprehension. Education in this case presents grave difficulties.

Case 18. Seen at age 55 months, this little girl was severely retarded in all directions, showing on examination a G.Q. of 31. She was slow on her feet with very poor carriage. She was beginning to be able to feed herself with a spoon. She had a small vocabulary of words and phrases. She could scarcely repond at all to Scales D, E or F.

In Fig. 14 will be found three more profiles: Nos. 19 to 21.

Case 19. This child presents a somewhat more hopeful picture than those we have just studied, although he also is severely retarded. At about 4½ years of age he had a General Quotient of 71. His results were fairly even across the profile except for Scale A. He was suffering from a right hemi-plegia.

It was a pleasure to test this child because of his remarkable persistence in a task, this was a quality that could not fail to impress the observer. He was friendly and interested in the toys and test materials, and responded well to everything he was asked to do. His total result was lowered by the unavoidable failure on Scale A. (Hemi-plegia).

When seen about a year later considerable all-round improvement had taken place. The same quality of persistence was observed. He showed determination to make his hands obey him, and carry out performance and other tests. He also showed a happy and pleasant personality, and appeared capable of further improvement.

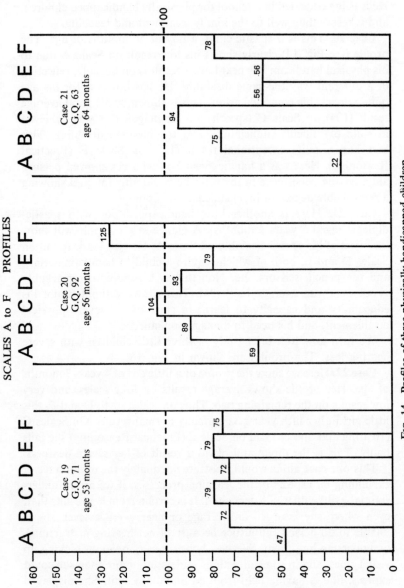

FIG. 14 Profiles of three physically handicapped children.

91

In 12 months he had raised his total level (G.Q.) from 71 to 80. He is being educated in a school for physically handicapped children, and is responding well to the kindly treatment and teaching.

Case 20. This is a spastic child, a boy of 56 months of age. The profile (see Fig. 14) clearly shows his low result on Scale A due to his physical handicap. His next lowest result is on Scale D, reflecting in a different way the same disability. He has however for his age quite remarkable comprehension. This is shown by his good average result (104) on Scale C (speech and language), this was achieved in spite of difficult enunciation, and troublesome dribbling. This boy had a quite exceptional result (125) on Scale F (Practical Reasoning). Here was a handicapped boy who yet showed personality, having persistence in the tasks he could attempt, and showing a remarkable degree of independence and courage.

Case 21. Here is another little handicapped boy with spastic-diplegia (aged 5 years 4 months). A glance at the profile will show the effect of his severe disability on Scale A. He also tends to fail on Scales D and E, both of which require a child to handle materials, and use pencil, scissors, etc. Nonetheless his speech is remarkably good, up to an average level (94). This shows without doubt his educability and capacity to learn, in spite of his severe physical disablement, and his need to manage appliances.

We turn now to a brief study of three little children with severe hearing loss. The profiles are shown in Fig. 16.

Case 22. Here we show the profile of a little girl of 4 years 7 months of age. Her profile shows average results on four scales, and very low results on the remaining two. Thus on scales A, B, D and E, this little girl in her fifth year gets perfectly normal results. On Scales C (Hearing and Speech) and on Scale E (Practical Reasoning) she fails badly. This is the direct and obvious result of her severe deafness.

This one case alone would illustrate adequately the importance of examining *all* aspects of the learning processes, if we are to understand the difficulties of a deaf child. It is certain from her results that, even where she is up to an average or near average level, she is unable to do herself full justice because of not hearing instructions, or understanding them. She was however very quick at picking up visual clues, and in some directions understood more than she could express. She is having help from an audiology unit. She displayed a playful and truly delightful personality.

Case 23. Here is the profile of another child with hearing loss. At 5½ years of age she is potentially a normal child, for on Scale A,

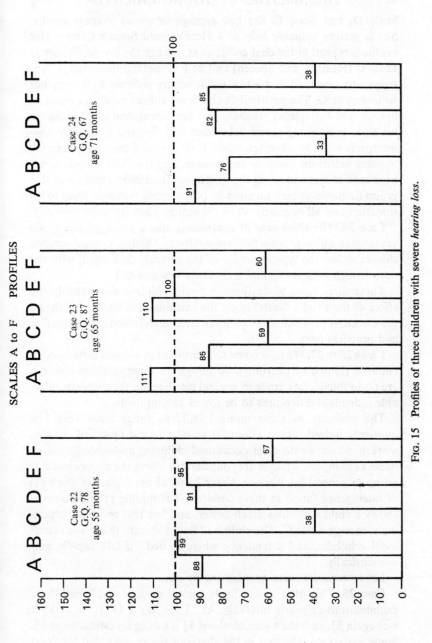

Fig. 15   Profiles of three children with severe *hearing loss*.

Scale D, and Scale E, she has average or above average results. She is getting valuable help at a Hearing and Speech Centre. Her profile is typical of the deaf child; as at this age the low results are at Scale C (Hearing and Speech) and at F (Practical Reasoning). It is frequently observed that a low result occurs at Scale B though not so low as at C. The personal-Social Scale suffers nearly as much as Speech and for similar reasons. The intelligent deaf child picks up his clues concerning social behaviour visually, and frequently mis-interprets what he observes. Scale F (Practical Reasoning) depends to some extent on question and answer, and the child who does not hear cannot respond to all the questions. Intelligent children of this group do however pick up clues by other senses that help them to do something on all or nearly all of the scales. They try quite valiantly.

Case 24. The third case of deafness is also a girl aged nearly six years. Not quite so able fundamentally as the last child described she yet shows the typical profile of the severely deaf child, with the deep trough at Scale C, and a similarly low one at F.

These three cases of deafness in young children show clearly the effect of the child's disability on the learning process. It also shows the direction in which these children need understanding, sympathy, and practical help.

Cases 25 to 27. We now come to a group of profiles of little mongol children (Down's Syndrome). Although all three of these children are undoubtedly low grade in general intelligence, there are consider-able individual differences to be found among them.

The majority of these mongol children range from very low quotients indeed, up to about 50 to 60 General Quotient. In this work however we do meet occasional children, undoubtedly classi-fiable as mongols, who yet are considerably above the majority of this group in general intelligence. Cases 25 to 27 are typical of the level of intelligence found in these children. The middle profile however shows a child who does much better, and her best result is surpris-ingly enough Scale C. The child had fluent speech, there was occas-ional echolalia, and a tendency when excited, to talk rapidly and nonsensically.

Let us consider these profiles one by one.

Case 25. This little one, a fairly typical mongol child, had three examinations at yearly intervals. At 2½ she had a G.Q. 53, at 3½ it was again 53, and when seen at about 4½ it was again estimated at 53. Some variations occurred in the shape of the profiles, but the total general level remained the same. This seems to bear out the hypo-

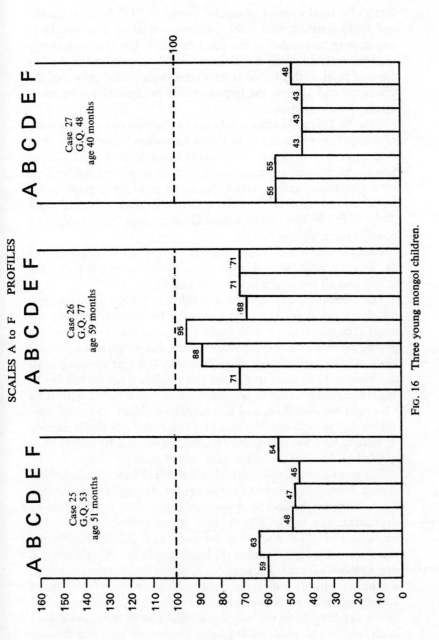

FIG. 16   Three young mongol children.

SCALES A to F   PROFILES

Case 25
G.Q. 53
age 51 months

Case 26
G.Q. 77
age 59 months

Case 27
G.Q. 48
age 40 months

thesis of a total amount of mental energy or "G" being available, and fairly constant with many children. Attention is turned from one activity to another as the child develops, but the total energy remains constant. With handicapped children, such as the deaf or cerebral palsied, this factor is interferred with by the effects of the disability, and also by the improvements brought about by treatments of various kinds.

Case 26. This child already referred to above, is one of those cases of mongolism where the child shows somewhat better ability, than is usual in this condition. She actually had a level of 95 (C.Q.) for Speech. Such cases are rare, but should be noted and followed up with systematic testing, for it would seem to be a gross social injustice not to give such a child a chance to show what she could do in an E.S.N. class. With a total Quotient over 70, this might be possible for a trial period.

Case 27. This is another child, a boy of $3\frac{1}{2}$ with a total quotient of 48. This is a really typical case, with a fairly even result across the scales, and all the results between 43 and 55.

The mongol child is pathetic. Lovable and fairly easily managed, his development is slow. The characteristic physical features are easily recognised by all who know these children. They present a genetic problem that is being studied in several places, and a growing body of information is becoming available. Whether anything at all can eventually be done to prevent this condition, we do not know. Meanwhile these children are members of our society, individuals who need consideration, and handicapped children who need care. Where they show themselves capable of accepting any useful training or tuition, however slight, or education, our advanced society must not fail to do what it can for each one of them.

The general problem of mental and physical handicap, is with us always. Now-a-days however the situation for many of these families where there are handicapped children is not quite so desperate or depressing, as it has been in the past. Many workers in the field of medicine and allied disciplines are using new techniques. Further discoveries of ways of helping the handicapped are being made and new methods adopted. The tendency now is to begin at the beginning, and have the little handicapped child under observation from earliest infancy onwards. From the hospital ward, to the welfare centre, and into every kind of clinic, the young child can be seen and helped according to the needs of the case. Paediatricians, psychologists, physicians of all groups, and many other workers, are aware of problems among babies and young children, arising from disabilities, many of which are diagnosed at or soon after birth, and treatment can often begin at a very early age. Thus the little deaf child can get some preliminary help during the first year of life. The child who is blind or has a visual defect, can be under observation, and the parents advised and helped in the training of the child. New groups of therapists have been trained to help the child and assist the parents by means of physiotherapy, speech therapy and other forms of treatment, working in conjunction with the relevent specialists, usually in hospital departments, or special centres.

The psychologist, play-therapist and remedial teacher, are also more alert to the needs of the very young, and are able to advise and guide parents in the education and general training of little children who may need special care or attention. Through detailed testing, such as that described in this book, follow-up studies can be undertaken, through a programme of re-testing in the home or school, or in the psychiatric clinic, child guidance centre, or hospital department, with advice all the time to the parents in the general management of the case.

In Part III of this book we shall set out the Test procedures for the six sub-scales of the Test, together with the necessary scoring standards.

PART III

ADMINISTERING THE EXTENDED SCALES

This colour photograph of the Apparatus was contributed by Dr. B. H. Burne of Amersham.

THE APPARATUS

CHAPTER X

ADMINISTERING THE SCALES
INTRODUCTION

BEFORE describing in detail the method of administering the six scales of the Total Examination under discussion, there are several preliminary matters to consider.

These are: 1. The general approach to the test situation.
2. The environment and properties.
3. The apparatus and its use in testing.

The most delicate part of the whole process of mental assessment relates to the earliest years of infancy. To get accurate and informative results with the youngest babies is a very subtle and difficult task, requiring considerable skill, and is quite different from the testing of older children. The examiner needs to be a close and sympathetic observer of little babies to be able to obtain accurate test results. This problem was fully dealt with in the earlier volume, "The Abilities of Babies", and any reader who would take up the testing of young infants is therefore referred to that work. Here however we shall still need from time to time to refer to these first two years of the tests to some extent, as these form the basic section of the entire scales, that now extend from birth to the eighth year of life, and into the ninth year. Nonetheless the present volume deals mainly with the testing of older babies and young children, and we shall need to pass somewhat rapidly over the first two years, to give space to fuller consideration of the problems of testing pre-school and infant school children.

These children varying from two to eight years of age for whom a mental test may be required are likely to be found in health and welfare centres, hospital departments, child guidance clinics and other clinics of various kinds, as well as in schools, having been referred for a test presumably because of a problem that needed investigation. Where much testing of these pre-school and infant school children, is likely to be needed, a special room equipped with toys, pictures and other properties suited to the ages of the children, would seem to be appropriate. Such background effects would help to create an attractive and reassuring atmosphere, for the child who might arrive in a somewhat apprehensive state.

Some of the equipment described earlier would be useful. A low table and chairs, in fact a nest of tables of varying heights, for use with children of different ages, and chairs to match, would overcome many difficulties. A trolley on wheels with two or three shelves for apparatus, so that it could be quickly brought up to the side of a table, or to a bedside, for the use of a child.

Taking into consideration the fact that these tests are useful with handicapped children, such as cerebral palsied children, and others who may be crippled, further special equipment in the testing room especially in hospital departments might be an advantage, or indeed a necessity if satisfactory results are to be achieved in a happy, relaxed atmosphere.

There would seem to be little need to emphasise the necessarily considerate and understanding attitude of those undertaking this kind of testing, for it is assumed that this important work will be placed only in the hands of qualified psychologists or doctors who have been trained in this kind of testing of children both normal and handicapped.

To come now to the actual testing apparatus, let us first look at the list of items used in the testing of babies under two years of age, and also used whenever, in testing an older child, it is necessary to go below the 24th month of the tests.

The Standardised Apparatus

Here then is the *list of the pieces of apparatus* used in testing babies below two years of age. (Griffiths Mental Development Scales, first two years). See "The Abilities of Babies", pp. 119-125 for a fuller description. (See colour plate).

1. A small coloured ball that rattles.
2. A small coloured rubber ball.
3. A brightly painted wooden ring with cord attached.
4. The bell-ring.
5. A pair of embroidery rings.
6. A small hand-bell.
7. A small electric torch.
8. A tuning fork.
9. A plastic cup and saucer.
10. A plastic teaspoon.

11. A pair of plastic beakers.
12. A small toy on wheels with cord attached.
13. A car to be pushed along (silent).
14. A car with motor.
15. A sleeping doll.
16. A mirror.
17. A small picture book.
18. A small wooden rod painted red.
19. A small plastic box for sweets.
20. A box containing twelve small toys.
21. A set of form-boards. 4 boards and 4 insets.
22. 4 yellow cubes in box.
23. A packet of paper tissues.
24. A set of brick-boxes: in three colours, each containing two bricks.
25. A set of 20 pictures mounted on cards.
26. A piece of coloured felt.
27. The screw toy.
28. A carrying case.

All these pieces should be available in the examination room, stored in a cupboard or drawer, and able to be locked away, or in the psychologist's test-box. These materials are mainly for the basic part of the test. However some of them are also used in further slightly more difficult items for older children. The following items of apparatus from the earlier set should therefore always be available whatever the age of the child to be tested.

These are: No. 2. The small rubber ball.
6. The hand-bell.
8. The tuning fork.
12. The pulling toy.
15. The sleeping doll.
17. The picture book.
20. The twelve toys in a box.
21. The little form boards.
24. The set of brick-boxes.
25. The 20 coloured pictures.
27. The screw toy.

The new items of standardised apparatus needed for testing children from 18 months old to 8 years, are now listed below.

Items needed for the Extension of the Scales

Scale A: 1. A skipping rope.
             2. A one-inch brick.
             3. A medium-sized ball, about the size of a tennis ball.

Scale B: 4. A buttoning test in box.
             5. Six extra objects for naming.
             6. A cord for tying knot.

Scale C: 7. The set of 20 small pictures.
             8. A large picture, mounted (country scenes).
             9. Ten colour plaques, in box.
           10. A set of capital letters.

Scale D: 11. Two pairs of scissors, and coloured papers.
           12. Beads and lace for threading.
           13. Ten yellow bricks, in box.

Scale E: 14. Nine brown bricks, in box.
           15. The six-hole board, with insets.
           16. The four-squares board, with insets.
           17. The eleven-hole board, with insets.
           18. The pattern making set. Bricks and booklet of patterns.

Scale F: 19 Two blue blocks (one larger than the other).
           20. Two weights.
           21. Small box containing coins.
           22. A clock face.
           23. The carrying case.

Note: A stop-watch is also needed for timing many of the tests.

In the next chapter we shall turn our attention to the method of administering the Locomotor Scale.

Note: **Record Forms** are available for scoring the entire range of tests for the First Two Years.

       Record Books, known as the *Blue Books*, are available for testing babies and young children from 0-8 years.

CHAPTER XI

ADMINISTERING THE TOTAL SCALES TO YOUNG CHILDREN FROM BIRTH TO THE END OF THE EIGHTH YEAR

As mentioned earlier the larger number of items in the first two years of the Scales as described in "The Abilities of Babies", should still be used when testing babies under about eighteen months of age. For this revised and extended Scale however, the items have been somewhat reduced in number, in accordance with the new scoring. This becomes necessary when this part of the Scale is used as the basic section of the total Extended Test, which now goes up to, and includes, the eighth year, and begins the ninth.

We shall now therefore present the entire range of tests, including this basic period, although it will seldom be necessary to go down to the test items of this basic period, when examining older children. Only exceptionally, perhaps when testing a deaf child, will it be necessary to explore so low into the basic section. As already explained some rearrangement of the order of test items, has resulted from the *larger samples* of children tested and the increased data thus available, which has been used in the more recent standardisation. The items, as they now stand, are placed in the strictest order of difficulty, as will be seen from the percentage tables (Chapter VI). Nonetheless whenever it is found necessary to go down to the items of the first two years reference should be made to "The Abilities of Babies" and the fuller description given there of individual items for this earlier period, and the method of administering them.

In scoring the items, the symbol ($\checkmark$) or minus ($-$) should be placed in the square provided in the Record Book.

ADMINISTERING THE LOCOMOTOR SCALE
SUMMARY OF ITEMS FOR THE FIRST TWO YEARS
SCALE A

The First Six Months (two items for each month of mental age)

Items

A.1.   *Pushes with feet against examiner's hands.*

With the child lying in the dorsal position, the examiner places his open hands without using any force, against the soles of the child's feet so that the child's knees are slightly flexed. The baby pushes with alternate feet or both feet together to remove the obstruction.

A.2.   *Lifts head up when prone.*

The child is able to lift his head well up. (25 to 40 degrees from the table).

A.3.   *Holds head erect for a few seconds.*

The examiner should take the child gently on to his knee, holding him in the sitting position, to observe whether the child can support his head a little.

A.4.   *Kicks vigorously.*

A.5.   *Lifts head in the dorsal position.*

The examiner takes the child's hands and *encourages* him to lift his head from the pillow, without pulling him up.

A.6.   The child's *back should now be firm* in the sitting position.

A.7.   *Lifts head and chest when prone.*

When placed in the prone position, the child can lift head, shoulders and chest, and can push himself up a little with his hands.

A.8.   *Holds head erect continuously.*

A.9.   *Lifts head and shoulders in the dorsal position.*

When the examiner now takes the baby's hands, the child can pull himself up a little, lifting head and shoulders.

A.10.   *Rolls from side to side.*

The child can now roll right over from one side to the other.

A.11.   *Crawling Reaction I.*

This is a definite stage in the crawling sequence. He is encouraged to crawl towards a ball or bright object. He struggles but makes slight progress.

A.12   *Sits with slight support.*

The child can now sit in pram or cot supported by pillows.

Second Six Months
Items

A.13. *Can roll from back to stomach, and from stomach to back.*
By the seventh month the average child can roll freely in almost any direction in search of toys etc.

A.14. *Crawling Reaction II.*
Tries vigorously to crawl.

A.15. *Sits alone for a short while.*

A.16. *Stepping reaction.*
The child can place one foot in front of the other when held up, with his feet in contact with a surface.

A.17. *Can be left sitting on the floor.*
The child can at this stage be left in a safe place, to play with toys.

A.18. *Stands when held up.*
The child is not expected to stand alone yet, but he can at this stage place his feet firmly when supported.

A.19. *Crawling Reaction III.*
Makes some progress forwards or backwards.

A.20. *Sits well in a chair.*

A.21. *Child can now pull himself up and stand holding on to furniture.*

A.22. *Crawling Reaction IV.*
Child can now creep on hands and knees.

A.23. *Side-steps around inside cot.*
Child can now walk round inside cot or playpen, side-stepping and holding on to rails.

A.24. *Can walk when led.*
Adult holding one or both hands.

Third Six Months
Items

A.II.1. *Can climb on to a low ledge or step.*

A.II.2. *Can stand alone.*

A.II.3. *Takes a few steps alone.*

A.II.4. *Can kneel on floor or chair.*

A.II.5. *Can climb stairs, up but not down.*

A.II.6. *Likes pushing a pram, toy horse etc.*

A.II.7. *Walks alone well.*
The child now not only walks alone, but trots well, with good balance.

A.II.8.　*Stoops.*

A.II.9.　*Develops a quick trot.*

A.II.10.　*Climbs into a low chair.*

A.II.11.　*Can walk backwards.*

A.II.12.　*Can walk pulling a toy on a string.*

Fourth Six Months
Items

A.II.13.　*Climbs stairs up and down.*
　　　　　The child at this stage is still *climbing*, not yet walking on the stairs.

A.II.14.　*Runs.*
　　　　　The child has at this stage superseded the more infantile 'trot' of a few weeks or months earlier. His movements have become a definite running.

A.II.15.　*Jumps.*
　　　　　The child can now make a little jump on the level floor, with both feet together.

A.II.16.　*Climbs to stand on a chair.*
　　　　　(An ordinary kitchen or dining chair is intended).

A.II.17.　*Walks upstairs.*
　　　　　Holding adult's hand.

A.II.18.　*Can seat himself at table*, if the chair is placed ready for him.

A.II.19.　*Can walk up and down stairs.*

A.II.20.　*Can kick a ball.*
　　　　　The child should be able to run a short distance or *walk to the ball and kick it without overbalancing.*

A.II.21.　*Can jump off a step*, both feet off the floor together. The child should be able to jump off the lowest step of a flight.

A.II.22.　*Can go alone on the stairs*, any method. Not necessarily in the upright position.

A.II.23.　*Can throw a ball into a basket.*
　　　　　The small ball should be used, and the child should stand about 2 feet away from the basket.

A.II.24.　*Can bring a chair* to the table, place it in position, *and seat himself* without help.

SCALE A.　LOCOMOTOR.　YEAR III

Items

A.III.1.　*Jumps off a step: both feet together.*
　　　　　At this stage, beginning of the third year, the child being more mature than for A.II.21 can be instructed to stand

with both feet together on the step and jump, landing also with both feet together. The 'quick step down' is superseded by a true 'jump', both feet reaching the floor simultaneously.

A.III.2. *Can stand on one foot for 6+ seconds.*

The child, who should be standing, is requested to raise one foot and stand on the other; the examiner must demonstrate if necessary. The child should raise one foot, either straight out in front of him or by bending the knee, and maintain a good balance on one foot for about 6 seconds.

A.III.3. *Can rise from kneeling without using hands.*

The examiner must encourage the child to kneel on the floor in an upright position (*not* sitting back on his feet), with his thighs in a straight line with his trunk. Then the examiner says smartly: "Now stand up; one, two!" and the child must be able to get up into the standing position *without touching* the floor or furniture or another person with his hands.

A.III.4. *Can cross both feet and both knees (sitting).*

The examiner places his own chair some distance from the child, and the child's chair as facing his. He then asks the child to sit down and, facing the child, himself seated, crosses one foot over the other and invites the child to do the same: "Can you do this?" . . . "See if you can cross *one foot* over the other". The exercise must then be done with the *other* foot and *both* must be satisfactory for a score.

Next, the child is asked to lift his leg and cross one *knee* over the other: right over left, then left over right. If the child does not understand what is wanted, the examiner should demonstrate.

All four positions should be scored, and anything unusual recorded.

A.III.5. *Can stand and walk tip-toe (6+ steps).*

(a) The examiner should demonstrate 'tip-toe' and the child must show good balance and maintain the position for about 5 seconds at least. If he wobbles about or tries to touch furniture, that is a failure.

(b) When the child has shown that he can *balance* on his toes (as above), he should straightaway be asked to keep on his toes and *walk* towards the examiner. *Standard:* 6 or more steps, keeping well up on toes and maintaining good carriage and easy balance. (We are looking for *good balance*. Weakness in these items may be very important in the diagnosis of the condition of certain handicapped children).

A.III.6.   *Stairs. Walk upstairs, one foot on each step, adult manner.*
In mounting stairs, little children at first put both feet on each step, and some may continue at this stage for a year or more. Next they learn to put one foot on each step, adult manner, when ascending the stairs only (not yet when descending). This adult stage when *ascending* the stairs scores plus at III.6.

SCALE A. LOCOMOTOR. YEAR IV

Items

A.IV.1.   *Can run fast indoors, or in a small outside space.*
This item needs very careful observation. A child under two years of age can 'run'. What is wanted here is to note if the child runs *evenly*, with *steady pace, good balance* and *firm* rhythmical placing of the feet. It is not so much the speed we want to observe as the normal manner of the running, energetic and confident. This can be a good diagnostic item where muscle weakness of any kind is suspected.

A.IV.2.   *Can ride a tricycle or other pedal toy.*
A child manages a tricycle at a surprisingly early stage.
To pass IV.2, the child must ride the tricycle *without help*. He must no longer need an adult to guide the machine, to push it or help to hold him on, etc.
If no tricycle is available for this test, the necessary information must be elicited from the child or the mother by careful questioning.

A.IV.3.   *Marches in time to music, etc.*
The examiner asks the child if he can march, and himself sings a well-known tune or claps hands in steady marching rhythm, showing the child what is wanted. The child should march some distance – all round the room, or round the table – keeping to the correct time.

A.IV.4.   *Can walk a chalk or painted line, at least 4 ft. long. (Two trials).*
At the research centre we have a line painted on the floor, 2 ins. wide. But the simplest method is to carry a two-inch piece of white chalk and, *using it on its side*, make a chalk line 2 ins. wide and six feet long on the floor.
The child should be able to place his feet fairly on the line so that the *middle* of his shoe covers it, and walk with reasonable balance. He must not step off, or over the edge, for a minimum distance of 4 feet, in order to succeed.

A.IV.5.   *Can hop on one foot* (3+ *steps*).

The examiner asks the child: "Can you hop?" If the child hesitates, say: "You can stand on one foot, can't you? Well, let me see you hop!" The child must make *at least three* consecutive hops, with the same leg raised throughout, and show good balance, to pass IV.5. (If necessary, the item should be demonstrated).

A.IV.6.   *Jumps off two steps.*

By the end of the fourth year or soon after, the average child jumps a great deal and can usually achieve this item. Again, his feet must be placed together and must reach the floor together.

Note that it is not wise to allow children being tested at this age (3+) to jump off *more* than two steps. They may want to "show off" their skills, but every care must be taken to avoid any accident; also, a fall or bump might put a child off the rest of the test. Older children can do so; but, if a child hesitates or refuses to jump, it is better to score minus and go on to the next item without comment.

SCALE A. LOCOMOTOR. YEAR V

Items

A.V.1.   *Can run to kick a ball.* (*Two trials*). The ball should be of about tennis ball size.

The child is placed about 10 feet away from the examiner, who puts the ball on the floor and remains near it (but to one side) in case the child slips. The child is instructed to run to the ball and kick it *without stopping running.* (Two trials).

Some little ones run up to the ball, stop, manipulate their position and then kick the ball from a stationary position. This is no more difficult than II.20 and is a failure at this level.

Other children run to the ball but fail to kick it, not being able to keep their eye on the ball when running. (This is a useful test of what might be called "foot and eye co-ordination". It is also a good test of body balance).

A.V.2.   *Stairs. Walks downstairs, one foot on each step.*

Early in the fifth year, about half our children can walk both upstairs *and down* in an adult manner, i.e. placing one foot on each step with confidence. This passes item A.V.2.

A.V.3.   *Touches toes, knees straight.*

Here, the child is in the standing position. Warn him to press his knees back; then say: "Now, just touch your shoes, keeping your knees straight". A second trial may be given if the child bends his knees. Bent knees are a failure. He must touch his toes with the finger-tips of both hands, with knees straight, to pass this item.

A.V.4.   *Jumps over a six-inch rope, both feet together.*

Using the rope provided, and if necessary tying one end to a table leg (etc.), the examiner or assistant holds the rope taut or straight at about 6 ins. from the floor. The child is instructed to *stand near the rope* with *both feet together* and jump over. His feet should remain together and he should alight on the floor with both feet together and both feet reaching the floor at the same moment. (There is no running up to the rope, no 'sag' in the rope, no quick-stepping over). Six inches is high enough for children of this age. Allow two trials. (See also A.VII.1).

A.V.5.   *Climbs on and off a bus unaided.*

Little children have to be lifted up on to a bus and carried down. The object of this item is to discover whether at this age the child can get on and off alone. This does *not* imply *travelling* alone, but just getting up the one or two high steps on to the bus; and it is a practical point in cities as so many children have to travel to school later on by bus or tram.

The child should be asked about this item, and the point confirmed whenever possible by asking parents or guardians.

A.V.6.   *Stairs. Can run upstairs.*

This is best observed on a tall staircase, and the adult should follow closely behind the child. Children begin to do this from about five years onwards. It must be a definite *run*, in the upright position and continuous for about 8+ steps. (No holding the banisters, or touching the stairs, is allowed).

SCALE A.   LOCOMOTOR.   YEAR VI

Items

A.VI.1.   *Can bounce and catch a ball.*

The examiner demonstrates this item by himself bouncing the ball lightly on the floor and catching it. Then the child is invited to try it. If the child catches the ball after bouncing it, he passes this item. (Two trials).

A.VI.2.   *Can run fast out of doors.*

This can best be observed when the child is free with other children in the playground. Otherwise, he should be taken outside at the end of the examination for this and certain other locomotor items. Again, what to look for is not so much great speed but a confident, steady, rhythmical movement. This item gives opportunity for observing anything unusual in the child's posture or running behaviour, or any physical defect affecting his movements. The normal child can, however, run quite fast at this age.

A.VI.3.   *Can throw a ball up (2+ feet) and catch it.*

This is another of the items best taken out of doors (or inside) at the *end* of the test.

The examiner takes the ball, throws it up *about 2 feet* and catches it again; then, giving it to the child, says: "Can you throw this ball up a little way and catch it again?" *Two trials* may be given. Some children throw the ball only a few inches up, to make sure of catching it. They should be encouraged to send it a little higher, to at least 1½ or 2 feet, to pass this item.

A.VI.4.   *Can hopskip 4+ steps.*

The examiner must demonstrate hopskipping if the child does not understand. At this age, most children can hopskip a short distance. The item can be taken indoors or outside, as most convenient. 4+ skips is enough to score plus at this stage; but, if the child is allowed to continue, he may pass items VII.2 and VIII.7. (q.v.).

A.VI.5.   *Can jump off three steps.*

Take as for A.IV.6, but, to pass at this stage, the child jumps off 3 steps. (See also A.VIII.2).

A.VI.6.   *Hopscotch I. One successful hop.*

This is a *very difficult* test and belongs to 6+ years.

The examiner may have to demonstrate it. A coloured one-inch cube is placed on the smooth floor (*not* carpet) and the child must place his foot near the brick and give a slight hop that sends the brick along but not too far. He must then hop after it and send it away again, and so on. The brick is "hopped", not kicked, along and the second foot must remain off the floor throughout. Two trials are allowed.

No child with muscle weakness or spasticity (even slight) could do this item. To pass VI.6, the child achieves *one* successful hop, sending the brick along. (See also A.VII.3).

Items   SCALE A. LOCOMOTOR. YEAR VII

A.VII.1.   *Can jump over a rope 10 inches high.*

When the child has passed A.V.4, the rope should be adjusted to give a taut line *ten* inches above the floor. The child is then invited to jump at this height. (Directions to the child as for A.V.4).

A.VII.2.   *Hopskips freely indoors* (12+ *skips*).

As for A.VI.4, but now the child can continue for at least 12 skips. If this item is taken outside, let him continue for at least 20 skips, he will then have passed item A.VIII.7 also.

A.VII.3.   *Hopskotch II. Two successful hops.*

As for A.VI.6, but now the child makes *two* successful hops, sending the brick along each time, hopping after it *with second foot up* throughout.

A.VII.4.   *Can run with steady trot some distance – all round play-ground or other outside space.*

A steady, rhythmical trot round playground or similar outside area is expected.

A.VII.5.   *Can skip with rope, turning for self.* (3+ *skips*).

Both boys and girls begin to skip somewhere in the seventh year, on average. The item is more popular with girls than boys, but boys can do this if encouraged. A boy who skips usually does so very well, and more often tries fast single skipping. (See below: A.VIII.5).

A.VII.6.   *Hopscotch III.*

At this stage, about half the children can manage 3 *hops*, each hop sending the brick along and the second foot kept off the floor throughout. (Two trials).

SCALE A.   LOCOMOTOR.   YEAR VIII

Items

A.VIII.1.   *Stairs. Runs downstairs.*

This is of course more difficult than running *upstairs*, because it is slightly more dangerous. The nervous child should on no account be urged to do this if he refuses.

A.VIII.2.   *Can jump off four steps.*

See notes for A.IV.6 and A.VI.5, but the standard now is 4 steps of an ordinary staircase.

A.VIII.3.   *Rides a bicycle* (*two-wheeler*).

Many children can ride a bicycle before they reach the eighth year, but this proves to be the age at which about half the children (50%) can ride a bicycle a short distance, or are just beginning to do so.

A.VIII.4. *Hopscotch IV.*

As for A.VII.6, but now the average child can manage 4 *hops*, each hop sending the brick along, while the second foot remains off the floor *throughout*.

A.VIII.5. *Fast single skipping.* (12+ *skips*).

Boys often do this fast skipping better than girls.

A.VIII.6. *Skips well.* (12+ skips) – ordinary double skipping.

Extra Items

A.VIII.7. *Hopskips some distance out of doors.*

As for A.VII.2, but child is now more confident and can continue hopskipping for some distance, at least 20 skips.

A.VIII.8. *Rides a two-wheeler with skill.*

To pass this item the child must be able to manage the machine without any help and ride about competently *in any safe open space.*

CHAPTER XII

ADMINISTERING THE PERSONAL-SOCIAL SCALE[1]

IN now approaching the Personal-social aspect of this work, the significance of this part of the assessment cannot perhaps be stressed too often. At first in earliest infancy the child is entirely dependent on the mother and other members of the family for all his needs, and is either at first unaware of people beyond the home, or is apprehensive at the approach of strangers, although this fear often differs considerably from child to child, and usually disappears during the first year.

As the baby develops and becomes more of an individual, differences in this regard between one child and another soon become more apparent. As the baby grows beyond the period of infancy, he shows a developing capacity to come into more friendly association with other children, and with adults. He also becomes more aware of the wider environment of home, nursery school, or nursery, and of the street, shops, and the total environment. In short, he gradually becomes emancipated from the extreme limitations of early infancy, and soon begins to develop a personality of his own.

As he enters the third year the young child develops a capacity to co-operate in play, with other children, and then goes forward to further social experiences. Parallel with this increasing social awareness he is also learning a degree of self-help, and with sympathetic training he gradually learns to manage many of his personal matters, such as learning to wash, dress, and feed himself.

In this chapter therefore we shall first present the somewhat revised items of the Personal-social Scale as previously standardised, and then continue with the new items of the extended Scale to the end of the eighth year of the tests.

[1] See also "The Abilities of Babies", pp. 153 to 165.

ADMINISTERING THE PERSONAL-SOCIAL SCALE

SCALE B

The First Six Months. (Two items for each month of age).

B.I.1.   *Quieted when picked up.* This is easily tested for, by lifting the child if he whimpers, or asking the mother to do so.

B.I.2.   Enjoys bath.

B.I.3.   Smiling. This usually occurs at about six weeks. It can be evoked by quietly talking to the child.

B.I.4.   Visually recognises mother. The examiner should step aside and ask mother to lean over the child, then a change of expression can usually be observed.

B.I.5.   Follows a moving person with the eyes.

B.I.6.   Returns examiner's glance with smiling or cooing.

B.I.7.   Frolics when played with.

B.I.8.   Resists adult who tries playfully to take the ring.

B.I.9.   Anticipatory movements when about to be lifted. (Generalised physical activity when the mother pretends to lift him).

B.I.10.   Turns head to person talking.

B.I.11.   Stretches deliberately to be taken.

B.I.12.   Drinks from a cup. (Cup supported by mother).

The Second Six Months

B.I.13.   Manipulates cup or spoon in play. The child should now be able to pick up the cup or spoon and play with it.

B.I.14.   Knows strangers from familiar friends.

B.I.15.   Shows prompt reaction to table and situations.

B.I.16.   Displeased if toy is taken away.

B.I.17.   Helps to hold cup for drinking. Now the child's hands come round the cup "helping" but he cannot yet manage the cup alone.

B.I.18.   Reacts to the mirror image: with smiling at, or playing with, the mirror image.

B.I.19.   Gives affection: returns an embrace or kiss.

B.I.20.   Finger-feeds. Can take up small pieces of food, with fine prehension.

B.I.21.   Waves bye-bye.

B.I.22.   Plays with cup, spoon and saucer, with comprehension.

B.I.23.   Plays pat-a-cake.

B.I.24.   Obeys simple commands: 'Give me cup', etc.

The Third Six Months

B.II.1.   Puts small objects in and out of cup in play.
B.II.2.   Tries to help with the dressing process: puts arm in coat, etc.
B.II.3   Can hold cup himself when drinking. (Credit as two
and 4.   items).
B.II.5.   Uses spoon fairly well: spills some.
B.II.6.   Shows shoes on request.
B.II.7.   Tries to turn door-knob.
B.II.8.   Likes adult to show book. Shows interest in pictures.
B.II.9.   Manages cup well half-full, holding it himself.
B.II.10.   Can take off own socks.
B.II.11.   Can take off own shoes.
B.II.12.   Uses spoon well, and feeds cleanly.

The Fourth Six Months

B.II.13.   Knows parts of the body (1) Indirect method, "Where are dolly's hands, etc." The six items are: hands, hair, feet, eyes, nose, mouth.
B.II.14.   Cleanliness: asks for attention.
B.II.15.   Bowel control complete.
B.II.16.   Knows parts of body (2).
B.II.17.   Tries to tell experiences.
B.II.18.   Bladder control by day.
B.II.19.   Knows parts of body (3).
B.II.20.   Asks for things at table by name.
B.II.21.   Parts, of body, now knows (4)
B.II.22.   Can open a door for himself.
B.II.23.   Helps actively with the dressing process.
B.II.24.   Begins to co-operate in play with other children.

SCALE B.   PERSONAL-SOCIAL.   YEAR III
Items
B.III.1.   *Gives first name on request.* (See also B.III.6).
            Quite tiny babies in their first year *respond to* their names, and in the second year give other definite evidence of "knowing their own names". Still later, the child can *say his name when he hears it*, but it is not until the third year that the average child can *tell* his own name *on request*.
            The examiner should ask: "What is your name?" and

record what the child says. It should be the correct first name, not a pet name, unless that is the only one used in the home.

If the child responds correctly, take item B.III.6.

B.III.2. *Uses spoon and fork together.* (See also B.V.3).

Children can themselves tell the examiner about this in conversation. While the toys are on the table (for item C.III.1) and the child is handling these, it is often possible to *observe* him pretending to eat with the little plastic *spoon, fork* or *knife*. This play should be encouraged, while the examiner observes carefully.

The examiner asks: "Do you use a spoon to eat your dinner at home?" If the answer is "No", ask: "Well, what *do* you use?" Some children can use *either* a spoon *or* a fork but not *both together* appropriately. Score plus *only if* he can use both together, one in each hand. Let the child demonstrate with the toy implements.

B.III.3. *Puts away toys when encouraged to do so.*

Again a 'line' can be obtained concerning this, by general observation and by letting the child pack all the little toys (C.111.I) back into the box.

He should also be asked about this in general. "Do you put your own toys away at home when mother asks you to?" etc. Confirm by asking mother.

B.III.4. *Knows sex.*

If the child is a boy, ask: "Are you a little boy or a little girl?" If the child is a girl, ask: "Are you a little girl or a little boy?" Silence, or a wrong response, should be noted.

B.III.5. *Can undo buttons.* (See also B.IV.1).

Still conversing with the child, ask him: "Can you look after yourself? Do you dress yourself? Can you undo buttons and do them up?" Then produce the buttoning test and ask him to *undo* the two buttons nearest to him. Say: "Never mind the other one. Now, can you do them up again?" If he succeeds, he also passes B.IV.1.

The child must on no account be allowed to pull at or drag on the buttons or the material. It is legitimate to show him *once* that the hand goes between the two pieces of cloth and the button must be put through the hole, or pushed out, with care.

B.III.6. *Gives family name.*

If the child has responded correctly to B.III.1, take B.III.6. Say: "That's right, have you another name?" By gently and judiciously conversing, the examiner can discover whether or not the child knows his second or family name.

SCALE B. PERSONAL-SOCIAL. YEAR IV

Items

B.IV.1. *Can do up buttons.* (See also B.III.5).

When the child has undone the two buttons (B.III.5), he should be asked to do them up again. He must do *both* buttons, without help, in order to pass.

B.IV.2. *Can put on socks and shoes unaided.* (See also B.V.5).

'Shoes' should be walking shoes, not slippers.

It is frequently possible to get this information correctly from the child by asking: "Can you put your shoes on by yourself?" If the child seems uncertain, ask "Who puts your socks on? ... Who puts your shoes on?" (etc.).

It may be necessary to ask the child to take his shoes and socks off, and see what happens. The heel of the sock sometimes gets on top of the foot, etc. To pass, the child should be able to put his socks and shoes on properly but not necessarily fasten the shoes up.

B.IV.3. *Knows age.* (Years old only expected).

Ask: "How old are you?" ... "You are getting to be a big boy (girl); how old are you now?" Only the number of years is required, e.g. "I'm three".

B.IV.4. *Plays well with other children.*

This is a later stage than B.II.24. The child should now enjoy playing *for quite long periods* with other children. His social adjustment can be studied by asking: "Do you like playing with other children?" "Are they nice to you?" and negatively: "Do they hit you?" etc. (See also B.VI.1).

B.IV.5. *Helps to lay table.*

Ask: "Do you help mother to put things on the table for tea?" (etc.). If the child answers very briefly, ask: "What do *you* put on the table?" Then after a pause. "Do you carry them from the kitchen?" or, "Does mother let you carry them?" "Who carries the tea things in?"

Or: "Can you lay the table? . . What do you put on it?" If the child gives clear evidence that he knows at least *three* things that go on a table for a meal and *helps* to put them there, this is sufficient for a pass at this stage. A gentle cross examination, supplemented by the child demonstating with the toys makes clear the stage he has reached.

B.IV.6. *Can undress self* (not difficult fastenings).

At this stage the child should be able to undress himself completely, except for really difficult fastenings, e.g. little boys cannot be expected to undo their own ties or difficult "zips", and little girls cannot undo frocks that fasten at the back.

SCALE B. PERSONAL-SOCIAL. YEAR V

Items

B.V.1. *Washes own hands and face.*

If the child is competent to do this on *all* occasions, and no longer heeds help, score plus.

Note: The examiner should question the child gently and carefully about the washing process, to be sure he has reached this degree of competence.

B.V.2. *Gives address* (2).

The examiner asks the child: "Where do you live?" Some children know their address only in part. If the child can give *two* of the usual three parts of an address (1. house, number or name; 2. street, lane, avenue, crescent, etc.; 3. district), he passes at this level. (See also B.VI.6).

B.V.3. *Uses knife and fork fairly well.* (See also B.VII.2).

Following B.III.2, there is an in-between stage when a child handles a knife and fork, one in each hand, fairly well, but uses the knife more as a "pusher" to put the food on the fork. We need to know whether the child has reached this stage only (if so, he scores plus at B.V.3); or whether he can *cut* the meat himself. (Stage of B.VII.2). The child should demonstarte with the plastic implements provided.

B.V.4. *Can dress and undress self.*

Again, not difficult fastenings. (See B.IV.6).

B.V.5. *Can fasten own shoe buckles.*

The child should now be able to fasten his shoe buckles without help.

B.V.6. *Manages top coat unaided.*

Ask: "Can you put on your biggest coat all by yourself?" etc. "And do it all up?" Opportunity to observe this will usually be found at the end of the interview, when the children are getting their coats, and putting them on.

SCALE B.   PERSONAL-SOCIAL.   YEAR VI

Items

B.VI.1.   *Has a special playmate.*

Following B.IV.4, the child now becomes more *selective* and if he can *name* a special friend that he plays with frequently, who perhaps lives near him (not a member of the child's own family), he would pass this item.

B.VI.2.   *Can tie a simple knot.*

Take the cord provided and tie a single knot in it *very slowly* and so that the child sees exactly what is done. Ask: "Can you tie a knot like that?" and, undoing it, also slowly, give it to the child and say: "Now, you try". (Two trials). *One* of two trials passes. Record result. (See also B.VII.1).

B.VI.3.   *Goes alone on simple errands to nearby shops, etc.*

and 4.   *Note:* In big cities a great deal will depend on where the child lives and whether there are busy roads to cross, etc. If he gives evidence of going alone on errands at this stage, he passes VI.3. (*Credit* as *two* items).

B.VI.5.   *Can brush and comb hair fairly well.*

This should be done nicely and with little or no help.

B.VI.6.   *Knows full address.* (3). (See also B.V.2).

At this stage the child must be able to give his full address, i.e. (1) name or number of the house; (2) the street, road, avenue, etc.; (3) the town, district, village, etc. He should be able to give this information clearly to a policeman if he were lost.

SCALE B.   PERSONAL-SOCIAL.   YEAR VII

Items

B.VII.1.   *Can tie a bow-knot* (1 loop).

When the child has made a knot in the cord (B.VI.2), the examiner should slip a pencil into the knot and tighten it. Then, using the pencil to keep the knot in place on the table, say (after demonstrating): "Now, make me a very nice bow" and see what the child can do – i.e. whether he fails completdly, or ties only one loop (which passes B.VII.1), or manages a double bow (B.VII.6).

B.VII.2.   *Uses a knife and fork competently:* cuts own meat.

Ask: "Who cuts up your meat?" (See also B.V.3).

B.VII.3.   *Shoes:* Child can tie own laces. Demonstrate.

(See also B.V.5) and (B.VII.6).

B.VII.4. *Efficient and competent at table.* (*Credit* as *two* items).

and 5. By this stage the child should be able to manage his meals in a cleanly way, using all the usual tools neatly, so that the parents can take him into a restaurant and he can manage everything efficiently, at almost adult level.

B.VII.6. *Can tie a bow-knot* (2 loops).

(See B.VII.1). A *double* bow passes at this stage, B.VII.6.

SCALE B. PERSONAL-SOCIAL. YEAR VIII

Items

B.VIII.1. *Can dress and undress completely.*

The child should at this stage require no help. He should be able to dress himself and undress, including all fastenings.

B.VIII.2. *Has one special school friend.*

(If the child names more than one special friend, he has probably not reached the stage of social development we are looking for, and does not pass this item).

B.VIII.3. *Takes full responsibility for hair.* (*Credit* as *two* items).

and 4. Both boys and girls must give evidence that they do at this stage take full responsibility for keeping their hair brushed and tidy at *all times.*

B.VIII.5. *Knows birthday – day and month.*

B.VIII.6. *Can lay a table completely,* with some supervision.

Test this with the small toys provided, supplemented by "indirect" questioning of the child, and the mother or teacher.

Extra Items

B.VIII.7. *Can lay a table completely, without help or supervision,* on all ordinary occasions.

B.VIII.8. *Knows full date of birth.*

Responds correctly to questions, i.e. day, month and year of birth.

CHAPTER XIII

ADMINISTERING THE HEARING AND SPEECH SCALE

COMING now to the Hearing and Speech Scale we shall first review the items used in the testing of babies under two years of age. A somewhat fuller description of these items has already been given elsewhere.[1]

Hearing and speech are matters of first importance in our studies of early childhood, and in the assessment of bright children, and also their less fortunate fellows who may be slow verbally for a variety of reasons, including the possibility of a degree of hearing loss. For children as they leave actual infancy and enter the period of early childhood this Scale fulfils two separate functions. On the one hand it should be a guide to the development of comprehension of language, as the child comes into constant contact with the social environment of his home, and later of school and the wider world. Secondly we can observe and measure, the growth and increasing complexity of sentence construction, from the babbled phrases of infancy, to the clear and logical sentences of slightly older children, and also the gradual inclusion, in the child's attempts to communicate, of different parts of speech. From the simple naming of objects beginning in the first year with "Mama, Dada, wow-wow, pussy" etc., nouns become more numerous and more meaningful, until by the third year other parts of speech are already in use, and beginning to be incorporated in the child's construction of sentences. Then, too, the actual length of such sentences is scored in the assessment, and so also is the multiplication of these different parts of speech.

The slightly modified items of the earlier version of the first two years of the Hearing and Speech Scales will be found below. These provide the basic period of Scale C which extends like all the other sub-scales to the end of the eighth year and into the ninth.

It is advisable when applying this scale, to make the fullest notes possible of the children's verbal responses, and provision is made for

[1] See "The Abilities of Babies", Chapter XIII.

this in the Record Book. This relates in particular to the full recodring, for example, of the responses to the "Big Picture", for such responses are evidence of the child's earliest capacity for composition. Some children speak at length, enjoying the picture, searching out as many objects as possible, and talking about them. However the time used in recording as much as possible of all this is well spent, for when the test is over evidence will be found in the responses to this one test item, of such matters as, 'Numbers of objects named', 'Parts of speech used', 'Length of sentences', 'Descriptive sentences' etc., which will enable a more complete assessment to be made. Therefore, everything said by the child in response to the picture should be recorded, and as much as possible of the child's verbal responses throughout the examination.

THE HEARING AND SPEECH SCALE
SCALE C

The First Six Months. (Two items for each month)

C.I.1.   Startled by sounds. The first item can be useful as a check on the child's hearing and general reaction to sounds.

C.I.2.   Vocalisation other than crying.

C.I.3.   Listens to bell. For this the little hand-bell is used and rung very gently about two-feet from the child and out of his field of vision. What is important to observe is whether the child quietens down if vocalising, or pauses to listen if active.

C.I.4.   Searches for sound with eyes.

C.I.5.   Makes two or more different sounds: e.g. a-a-a, la, oo, mmm, etc.

C.I.6.   Listens to music.

C.I.7.   Searches for sound with head movements. Small searching movements of head and eyes are observed when the bell is rung softly, or other sounds occur.

C.I.8.   Listens to tuning fork. The hearing child listens intently.

C.I.9.   Turns head deliberately to the bell.

C.I.10.   Coos or stops crying on hearing music.

C.I.11.   Babbles to persons. Early beginning of communication by vocal sounds.

C.I.12.   Makes 4+ different sounds.

The Second Six Months

C.I.13.   Responds when called. If quiescent the hearing child becomes active, or he may respond vocally.

C.I.14. Two syllable babble emerges, e.g. aga, oogoo, looloo.
C.I.15. Listens to conversations.
C.I.16. Babbled phrases of 4+ syllables. Speech is gradually developing, sounds are being combined, and babbled syllables joined into phrases.
C.I.17. Says Mama, Dada, etc. One word clear.
C.I.18. Listens to stop-watch.
C.I.19. Rings the bell.
C.I.20. Shakes head for 'No'.
C.I.21. Says two clear words, used appropriately.
C.I.22. Babbled sentences of six plus syllables. Speech is now developing rapidly.
C.I.23. Babbled monologue when alone.
C.I.24. The average child now has three clear words at this age—12 months.

Third Six Months
C.II.1. Looks at pictures for a few seconds. Children like the coloured pictures, and may even *try* to turn the pages of the little book.
C.II.2. Tries definitely to sing.
C.II.3. Knows own name.
C.II.4. Likes rhymes and jingles.
C.II.5. Looks at pictures with increasing interest.
C.II.6. Uses four clear words.
C.II.7. One object in the box of toys *identified* when named by the examiner.
C.II.8. Uses five clear words appropriately.
C.II.9. Long babbled sentences occur, with occasional clear words.
C.II.10. Enjoys picture book, turning the pages and talking at the pictures.
C.II.11. The average child has now a vocabulary of six or seven words.
C.II.12. Two objects in the box of toys are *identified*.

The Fourth Six Months
C.II.13. The child now uses nine+ clear words.
C.II.14. Four objects in the box can now be *identified*.
C.II.15. Picture vocabulary: One picture can now be correctly named.
C.II.16. Uses twelve clear words.

C.II.17. Word combinations now occur.[1]
C.II.18. Picture vocabulary: Two pictures correctly named.
C.II.19. Uses 20+ clear words.
C.II.20. Eight objects in the box *identified*.
C.II.21. Listens to stories.
C.II.22. *Names* four objects in the box.
C.II.23. Picture vocabulary 4.
C.II.24. Uses sentences of four or more syllables.

SCALE C.   HEARING AND SPEECH.   YEAR III

Items

C.III.1. *Names twelve objects in box.*

Produce the little box of toys and the six other small objects.

There are 18 altogether – the 12 used in the second year plus 6 others. Let the child handle the toys and chatter as he plays with them. Note the ones named, then check up by asking him: "What is this?" etc. *Do not name* the objects for him at this stage. Record the number correctly named. Identification should not now be used; the child must *name* the objects.

Continue the conversation, doing item C.III.3 and certain other tests (e.g. C.IV.2) whilst the child is still happy with the toys.

C.III.2. *Picture Vocabulary* (12).

The child has to *name* the objects in the pictures (the twenty small pictures which are numbered in order of difficulty). Babbled names can be accepted only if they are well known and likely to be used in the home: e.g. "wow-wow" for "dog", "pussy" for "cat", etc. Imamturity, such as "'poon" for "spoon" is scored plus but these immature words should be recorded.

Show the pictures one at a time in correct order, as numbered; stop if the child fails six pictures consecutively. For this item score 12+ as correct. (See also C.IV.5).

C.III.3. *Defines by use* (2+). (See also C.V.1).

Following C.III.1, and whilst the toys are still on the table, ask: "What do we have a cup for?" ... "What does a knife do?" ... "What do I want a chair for?", etc. Note the number correctly answered, even if in monosyllables, e.g. "What does a knife do?" – "Cuts".

---

[1] Note re word combinations. These constitute a stage that precedes the true sentence, and involves using 2 *words* together in a short meaningful phrase. Examples are: "Daddy gone"; "More milk"; "Get down", etc. See "The Abilities of Babies", p. 181, item C.46.

C.III.4.   *Repeats a six-syllable sentence.* (Record Booklet, page 10).

Say: "Listen! I want you to say something for me . . . Listen! Say this . . ." Then give the three little sentences for C.III.4 *one* at a time. Note how many the child can say *quite* correctly, and what errors he makes, if any. Some children get only the last word; in this case it is sufficient to underline that word, which will indicate that: 'He said only this last word'.

If the child repeats the six syllables of *one* sentence easily and correctly, he passes this item. The sentences are:

(i) "I have a little cat"
(ii) "My pussy caught a mouse"
(iii) "The mouse had a long tail".

C.III.5.   *Uses two or more descriptive words.* (See also C.VI.3).

These should be listened for in the child's conversation but more particularly in relation to his description of the large picture (item IV,1), where descriptive words, etc. should be underlined in the child's account (i.e. adjectives and adverbs).

C.III.6.   *Talks in sentences of 6+ syllables.*

At just two years old, the child uses short sentences of four+ syllables. At this later level, longer sentences are expected: six+ syllables. Speech should in general be fluent. Examples of sentences used by the child during the examination should be recorded. (See Record Book, page 10).

Babble should by this age be entirely left behind, although perfect pronunciation cannot be expected.

SCALE 6.   HEARING AND SPEECH.   YEAR IV

Items

C.IV.1.   *Names 6+ objects in large picture.* (See also C.V.6).

Produce the large coloured picture and ask the child to "tell all about it". Encourage him, but do not point out objects, or question him about details. One might say, for example, "What can you see? . . . What are they all doing?" *Everything* the child says should be *recorded* (Record Book, page 10), and on the basis of this record several other items can be scored. In this complete record of what the child says, the examiner should underline nouns, descriptive words, pronouns, descriptive sentences. (See examples of responses to pictures, pp. 133 & 134).

C.IV.2.   *Names 17 or 18 objects in box.* (See C.III.3).

At this stage, the child should know and name not only the *twelve* objects given earlier but *five or six* of the additional six items (i.e. knife, fork, saucer, watch, key, pencil). As before (C.III.3), the examiner asks, showing each object: "What is this? What do we call it?".

C.IV.3. *Uses personal pronouns correctly* (2+). (Record Book, p. 10)
Following CIV.1, underline any personal pronouns (I, you, he, they, etc.) used by the child in his description of the picture, and add to these any the child has used at any time during the test. (See also C.IV.5).

C.IV.4. *Comprehension* (2+ *items*). (Record Book, p. 11).
Refer to the question on page 11 of the Record Book and ask them in the order given. *Two correct* scores plus at this level. (See also C.VI.2 and C.VIII.3) e.g. "What should you do if you feel tired?" etc.

C.IV.5. *Picture Vocabulary* (18+). See C.III.2).
The child should now name *eighteen* of the twenty pictures to pass this level.

C.IV.6. *Knows six colours*
Produce the ten little coloured plaques and (beginning with red) ask: "What colour is this? . . . What do we call this colour?" etc. Note the ones failed and score the number passed. *Six or more* scores plus at this level. (See also C.VI.6).

SCALE C. HEARING AND SPEECH. YEAR V

Items

C.V.1. *Defines by use* (6+). (See also C.III.3).
For the objects, see Record Book, p. 12, e.g. cup, knife, chair, coat, car, etc. The child should now answer *six* or more questions correctly.

C.V.2. *Opposites* (2). (See Record Book, p. 11).
Just say: "Listen to this: 'A boy is big, a baby is . . .?' " etc.
The first two of these are fairly easy and belong to this level. The third is deliberately much harder and belongs to the eighth year. (See C.VIII.6).

C.V.3. *Materials* (2+).
Table, window, house. Ask: "What is a table made of?" "What is a window made of?" "What is a house made of?"

C.V.4. *Repeats sentences of* 9 *or* 10 *syllables*. (See page 10).
Say: "I wonder if you can say this. Listen!..."
(i) "My dog is a very good friend to me"
(ii) "I take my dog when I go for a walk".
Score plus only if *one* sentence is *quite* correct.

C.V.5.   *Picture Description: One or more good descriptive sentences.*
Use the large picture, as for item C.IV.1.

At this higher stage, the child should *describe* the picture in good sentences, not merely enumerate the objects in it. If a full record was made earlier of the child's response, underline those sentences that contain genuine descriptive matter. *One* good sentence scores plus at C.V.5.

C.V.6.   *Names* 12 *objects in large picture.* (See C.IV.1).
To pass C.V.6, the child should have named *twelve* or more objects in the large picture.

SCALE C.   HEARING AND SPEECH.   YEAR VI

Items

C.VI.1.   *Talks in sentences of* 10+ *syllables* (page 10).
The examiner should engage the child in conversation (encourage him to talk about his play activities, toys, friends, etc.) and note the length of sentences used by him. This can also be noted in relation to the description of the large picture.

Early in the sixth year, the average and above average children are quite fluent and can produce sentences of this length (10+ syllables) and longer. These should of course be grammatical sentences and not just strings of isolated words or phrases as used by younger children.

C.VI.2.   *Comprehension* (4 *items*). (See also C.IV.4 and C.VIII.3).
The standard here is *four* of the comprehension questions correctly answered. (Record Book, page 11).

C.VI.3.   *Uses* 6+ *descriptive words* (adjectives, adverbs). (See also C.III.5).
Refer to the child's own description of the picture for these, and add any others used by him in general conversation.

C.VI.4.   *Names* 10+ *capital letters.* (See also C.VII.3 and C.VII.6).
Take the box of letters; tip them out on the table and let the child name those he knows. He should say the *name* of the letter, not give the phonetic sound only. It is permissable to say: "Tell me the *name* of this letter; I don't want just to hear the sound it makes", etc. Record the number correctly named.

C.VI.5.   *Uses* 6+ *personal pronouns.* (See C.IV.3).

C.VI.6.   *Names* 10 *colours.*
Take as directed for item C.IV.6. The child should know the names of *all* the ten colours to pass at this level.

SCALE C. HEARING AND SPEECH. YEAR VII

Items

C.VII.1. *Repeats a sentence of* 16 *syllables*. (See C.V.4).

The sentence to be repeated is:

"It will be my birthday next week; Mother will give me a party". The sentence must be repeated without error, or omission etc. (See Record Book, page 10).

C.VII.2. *Picture Description:* 3 *sentences*. (See C.V.5 and VIII.1).

At this stage, early in the seventh year, *at least three* good sentences of a descriptive quality are expected, in response to the picture.

C.VII.3. *Knows* 20+ *capital letters* and names them when shown.

See the earlier stage (C.VI.4) and later item (C.VII.6).

C.VII.4. *Similarities* (1) (page 11). (See also C.VIII.2 and C.VIII.5).

Say: "You know a carrot, and you know a turnip? Tell me how they are *like* one another". Similarly with: tiger and cat, penny and button, a tree and a daisy. *One* correct scores plus.

C.VII.5. *Differences* (2). (See also C.VIII.4 and C.VIII 7 and 8).

Say: "You know a fly, and you know a bee? They are not both alike, are they? How are they different?"

Proceed in the same way with: ice and glass, string and rope, salt and sugar. *Two* correct scores plus. (Record Book, page 11).

C.VII.6. *Names* 26 *capital letters*. (See C.VI.4 and C.VII.3).

To pass this item the child should name correctly *all* the letters, when shown them.

SCALE C. HEARING AND SPEECH. YEAR VIII

Items

C.VIII.1. *Picture Description:* 4 *sentences*. (See also C.V.5 and VII.2)

To pass this, the child should produce *four* good descriptive sentences (page 10 of Record Book), in response to the picture.

C.VIII.2. *Similarities* (2).

As for VII.4 above, but now the standard is *two* to pass.

C.VIII.3. *Comprehension* (6).

As for VI.2 but the standard is now *six* questions correctly answered.

C.VIII.4. *Differences* (3).

As for VII.5 but *three* questions must be answered to pass at this level.

C.VIII.5. *Similarities* (3).

As for VII.4 (and C.VIII.2), but now *three* must be passed.

C.VIII.6. *Opposites* (3). (See Record Book, p. 11 and C.V.2).

Extra Items

C.VIII.7 ⎫ *Differences* (4). (See C.VII.5 and C.VIII.4).
and 8. ⎭ *All four* correct. (*Credit* as *two* items).

Let us now conclude this chapter by quoting actual responses to the large picture:

RESPONSES TO LARGE PICTURE

With further reference to the items associated with the large picture it is important to write down in the place provided in the Record Book (top of page 10) *everything* the child says in response to the picture that is: "naming objects in the large picture" (names 6+ objects at C.IV.1, names 12+ objects in large picture at C.V.6) and also using one or more descriptive sentences at C.V.5, C.VII.2 and C.VIII.1. From this one record if carefully and fully made a number of items can be scored. The younger children respond in mono-syllables or single words. Errors in pronunciation or diction should be ignored for this purpose but numbers of separate items named from the picture, length of phrases and sentences noted, and with the abler children descriptive sentences give further credits.

A few examples might be useful, those now following are taken from actual records of children tested.

1. Responding in mono-syllables and single words, e.g. item C.IV.1 (names 6 or more objects in large paicture). Actual responses from the records: "lady", "dog", "water", "girl", "a duck", etc. It is quite ligitimate to say to the child, "That's very nice, what are they doing?" Then the child may either (a) name a few more items in the picture or (b) begin to speak in phrases or short sentences, e.g. "Boys on bike", "Mummy go shopping", "Lady got basket", "Dog running". If at this stage the child produces a short sentence, but one that is truly descriptive and of *at least* 6 *syllables in length*, he passes at V.5. Examples would be, "The dog is running after the bike", "The kite is going up high", "That boy is fishing in the pond", "The postman is taking a letter to that house", "The mother is going shopping" etc. If the child continues and produces 3 such sentences he passes at VII.2 and if he gives a truly fluent series of descriptive sentences of at least 4, he passes at V.III.1.

Examples of responses are given below:

They are all taken at random from the records of children in their seventh year, 2 boys and 2 girls.

1. Boy in his 80th month of age, resident in a children's home. "Two boys was riding on motor bikes. They were looking down at their wheels. A boy and girl was running with their dog and their Granny want that dog, and so they brought a donkey. They was diving into the sea and a wee boy was catching a fish and 2 swans was looking at the boy who was fishing. All the birds was flying along – away – far! They saw the chapel, the chapel was fairly long, and the donkey stood looking at the baby and the wee boy. The cross was standing up there up on the chapel roof – high!"

Scoring: Sentences of good length pass VI.1.[1]

Objects named pass V.6.

Descriptive words VI.3.

Personal pronouns and possesives IV.3.

Descriptive sentences VIII.1.

Note: G.Q. total scale 93.

I.Q. Terman Merrill 80.

2. Girl in her 80th month tested in North London. "There's two boys riding on two bikes and there's a little girl and a little boy running, and there's a donkey. Another little girl has a yellow dress and white hat. And a mother and her little baby. There's another mother with a yellow basket and her doggy. There's two white pigeons. There's fourteen trees and there's a little boy fishing with a big yellow bag. There's flowers with a stick in the middle. There's six houses and a man, his trolley, I think (wheelbarrow). There's another little girl playing with her kite. There's eleven birds, and there's a church, and there's two white clouds".

Scoring: Sentences of good length pass VI.1.[1]

Objects named passes V.6.

Descriptive words VI.3.

Personal pronouns IV.3.

Descriptive sentences VIII.1.

Note: G.Q. total scale 111.

I.Q. Terman Merrill 111.

3. Girl in her 80th month. This child begins: "Gipsies. Caravan. Horse, baby, basket, wheels, windmill".

Examiner interjects: "That's very nice, tell me all about it". The child continues:

"A little boy is riding the caravan and a man is pulling the horse.

1 Standard: 10 syllables or longer.

There's another horse that the little girl is riding in the field; and there's a dog behind the caravan. And the old lady is carrying a basket full of flowers. And the lady with the baby has got some flowers as well. And there's a horse with a dog in the garden".

Scoring: Sentences of good length pass VI.1.
            Objects named passes V.6.
            Descriptive words III.5.
            Descriptive sentences VIII.1.

Note: G.Q. total scale 105.
        I.Q. Terman Merrill 101.

4. Boy in his 81st month. This little chap begins every sentence with "there are" or "they are". His sentences are crisp and complete. He is about 1 month older than the other three children whose "picture description" has just been given.

He begins: "There are two cows red, and one black and white and one white and red. The two red cows have one white horn each. There are a little red bird in the tree. There are a scarecrow in the fields to scare the birds away. Chicks and hens and calves they are in the field and cows. There are haystacks for next winter. The farmer drives the cows into the fields and locks them up. The skies are blue and there's birds in the air. There are purple flowers just outside the gate. There are hot milk from the cows, just after being milked. The cow that is black and white, has one ear and one horn. There's a ladder lying against the haystack. There's a postman just going to post a letter in the door. See trees, some are dark green and some are light green and some are black. They are a little yellow bird this time sitting on the gate singing. They are big white birds in the air. One chimney is smoking".

Scoring: Sentences of good length pass VI.1.
            Objects named pass V.6.
            Descriptive words VI.3.
            Descriptive sentences VIII.1.

Note: G.Q. total scale 99.
        I.Q. Terman Merrill 105.

CHAPTER XIV

ADMINISTERING SCALE D:

HAND AND EYE CO-ORDINATION

WE shall, in this Chapter, as in previous sections, begin with the revised items for the first two years, and the reader is as before referred to "The Abilities of Babies" for the fuller details of the earlier version of the Hand and Eye Scale.

In the very early stages after the birth of a baby the eyes show little co-ordination with the hands. Gradually the baby learns to fixate and to follow objects, and these visual items form the early part of Scale D. At the same time the baby's hands are also active, and the child learns to grasp and hold toys, but does not at first *look* at what he is holding. As soon as he begins to do so it can be said that eye-hand co-ordination has begun and will continue to develop towards true grasping and manipulation. The earliest grasping and holding is measured in Scale E, and these early items will be found in that section. These items that measure hand behaviour were deliberately separated so that the possibility of a defect of vision could be studied on the one hand, and any untoward weakness of manipulation could also be observed and separately recorded. It is important to look closely at the developing hands and this aspect was carefully standardised and forms the early part of Scale E.

As before the reader will find below all the items of the revised Scale D for the first two years, and then we shall pass on to the Extended part of this Scale also.

A large number of the test items of Scale D relate to the child's capacity to depict his ideas through drawing, and as will be seen a number of formal drawing tests are also included. The necessary scoring standards for each of these drawings will be found below.

SCALE D

First Six Months. (See "The Abilities of Babies", p. 187).

D.I.1.　　Follows a moving light with the eyes. (A small low-powered torch is used for the study of eye movements).

D.I.2.   Looks at the wooden ring momentarily. Momentary fixation.
D.I.3.   Follows the slowly moving ring horizontally.
D.I.4.   Follows the slowly moving ring vertically.
D.I.5.   Follows the slowly moving ring in a circle.
D.I.6.   Glances from one object to another.
D.I.7.   Watches object pulled along by string, on the table surface.
D.I.8.   Visually explores new environment. The child at this age looks around in a new environment.
D.I.9.   *Reaches* for ring when offered, grasps and retains it.
D.I.10.   Secures the dangling ring.
D.I.11.   Hands explore the table surface.
D.I.12.   Plays with ring, shaking bells, etc.

Second Six Months
D.I.13.   Looks for dropped toy.
D.I.14.   Strikes one object with another.
D.I.15.   Partial specialisation of thumb and forefinger now present.
D.I.16.   Secures the ring by means of the string.
D.I.17.   Fine prehension. This can be observed by the way that the baby picks up the string, or a sweet pellet should be used to observe the presence of the pincer movement of the thumb and forefinger.
D.I.18.   Dangles the ring by the string.
D.I.19.   Throws objects.
D.I.20.   Thumb opposition complete.
D.I.21.   Can point with the index finger.
D.I.22.   Interested in toy motor-car.
D.I.23.   Can hold pencil as if to mark on paper.
D.I.24.   Likes holding on to little toys.

Third Six Months
D.II.1.   Uses a pencil on paper a little.
D.II.2.   Shows preference for one hand.
D.II.3.   Plays rolling a ball on table or on floor.
D.II.4.   Can hold 4 cubes in hands all at once, two in each hand.
D.II.5.   Plays pushing little cars along.
D.II.6.   Places one lid, box, or brick upon another.
D.II.7.   Tower of 2 bricks: shown by examiner.
D.II.8.   Pulls cloth to get toy.
D.II.9.   Scribbles more freely.

D.II.10 Constructive play with boxes or other materials.
and 11. (Credit as two items).
D.II.12. Builds a tower of three bricks (not shown).

Fourth Six Months
D.II.13 Can throw a ball.
and 14. (Credit as two items).
D.II.15. Can now build a tower of four bricks.
D.II.16. Enjoys vigorous straight scribble.
D.II.17. Can pour water from one cup to another.
D.II.18. Can build a tower of five bricks.
D.II.19. Circular scribble in imitation. (See Fig. 17).
D.II.20 Makes a train of three+ bricks.
and 21. (Credit as two items).
D.II.22. Makes brick or toy walk.
(Imitative play reaction).
D.II.23. Builds a tower of six or seven bricks.
D.II.24. Draws a perpendicular stroke.

SCALE D. HAND AND EYE CO-ORDINATION
YEAR III

Items
D.III.1. *Makes a horizontal stroke.*
The examiner should draw the child's attention to the
horizontal stroke printed in the record book (page 6) and
encourage the child to make such a stroke. He may be shown if he
does not understand.
D.III.2. *Threads 6 beads.* (See also D.IV.2 and D.VI.1).
The examiner should have, ready for the test, twelve beads
threaded on a lace, the end ones tied in, in the following
pattern: 3 green, 3 red, 3 yellow, 3 blue, and also a similar string
with only *one* bead threaded and tied on. The examiner shows these
to the child and draws his attention to the arrangement of the beads
in this pattern, and also indicates that the first *green* bead is already
tied on *his* string, which the examiner then gives him.
The pattern is left on the table for the child to follow. If he
goes ahead in his own way, threading but ignoring the pattern, it is
legitimate to say: "Look at the pattern", once or twice. No other
urging may be made. For D.III.2 it is sufficient if the child threads
6 or more beads and ignores the pattern. (See also D.IV.2 and D.VI.1).

D.III.3. *Builds a tower of 8+ bricks.*

Following D.II.23, if the child has built up 7 bricks, encourage him to continue; or, if the tower collapses, let him try again; and if he then builds a tower of 8 *or more* bricks he passes D.III.3.

D.III.4. *Handles scissors – tries to cut.* (See also D.IV.3.)

The examiner picks up his own paper (4 ins. square) saying: "See, I am going to cut my paper in half". He proceeds to do so. The child then takes scissors and tries to cut *his* paper in half also. Some children have little idea of how to handle the scissors – holding them in such a way that the blades will not open, or in both hands so that they will not close. These are both failures.

The child who gets the paper between the blades and tries but fails to cut, or cuts in a wavy direction, or causes the paper to fold over a tear, passes D.III.4 ('tries'), but not D.IV.3.[1]

D.III.5. *Copies a circle* – primitive model – Stage I. (Fig. 19).

The drawing of a circle in the booklet (page 7) should be shown, the examiner saying: "Look at what you are going to make now: a ball". Then the examiner invites the child to try,

Score plus for D.II.19
Examples of circular scribble

FIG. 17

1 Note: The scissors used are safe for young children, being kindergarten scissors and with rounded ends.

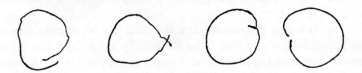

Scoring Standard: Satisfactory at Stage I
D.III.5   Copies a circle   Stage I
FIG. 18

indicating the place where his attempt should be made. It is quite legitimate to say "Stop when you have finished", so as to restrain the young child from his desire to continue circular scribbling (which would pass only at stage D.II.19).

A certain amount of self-control is required of a two-year-old to *stop* when he has completed the circle. The standard here is higher than that of the circle in the Terman-Merrill at this age level. (See scoring standards). Nonetheless, a rough circle is all that is expected and it need not be neatly closed (See also D.V.2).

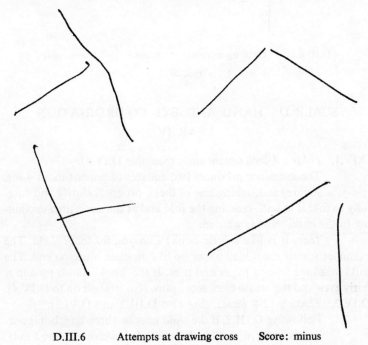

D.III.6   Attempts at drawing cross   Score: minus
FIG. 19

D.III.6. *Copies a cross (recognisable).* Stage I (page 7). (See also D.V.1).

It is best to recapitulate if the child has not already drawn the perpendicular and horizontal strokes, by letting him first draw these. Then, showing the printed drawing of the cross in the Record Book, indicate where the child should make his cross. If he manages *deliberately* to make one line cross over another, however inadequate the actual drawing, he passes at this level. (Fig. 20).

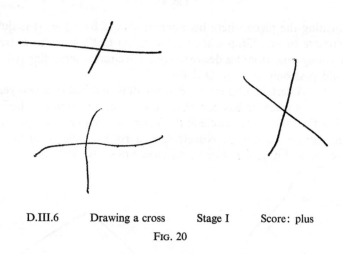

D.III.6   Drawing a cross   Stage I   Score: plus

FIG. 20

SCALE D. HAND AND EYE CO-ORDINATION
YEAR IV

Items

D.IV.1. *Folds a 4-inch square once.* (See also D.IV.4).

The examiner produces two squares of paper (about 4-ins. square) and, taking one of these, proceeds slowly and carefully to fold it in half, creasing the fold and at the same time explaining to the child what is wanted.

"See, it is like a little book! Can you do that?", etc. The examiner stands the folded paper up like an open book on end. The child takes the second paper and tries. If the 'book' stands up and is fairly even and the crease firm, score plus. (Go straight on to D.IV.4).

D.IV.2. *Threads 12+ beads.* (See also D.III.2 and D.VI.1).

Following D.III.2, if the child goes on threading, but ignoring the pattern, until he has threaded twelve or more beads, he passes at this level.

D.IV.3. *Can cut a square into two pieces.* (See also D.V.6).

Following D.III.4, if the child cuts the square of paper fairly neatly in half, he pasess this item. If the cut is very crooked or far from the centre, it must be failed.

D.IV.4. *Folds 4-inch square twice.*

Following D.IV.1, if the child has made a fairly good attempt at the first fold, he is invited to fold the square again: "Fold it like a letter", the examiner folds his "like a letter" to show what is wanted. Again, the standard is fairly high. The second fold must be carefully creased and the paper neatly folded into four.

D.IV.5. *Copies a ladder* (recognisable). (Stage I). (Record Book, page 14).

The examiner shows the printed drawing of a ladder and indicates where the child's drawing is to go. The standard is not high at this level, but the drawing must be clearly recognisable as a "ladder". (See D.VII.2 for stage II). See scoring standards (Fig. 29).

D.IV.6. *Draws a man* (recognisable). (Stage I). (Fig. 28).

Say to the child "Can you draw a man? . . . Draw Daddy", etc. Let the child make his attempt in the booklet (page 7). There are *three stages* standardised here: at D.IV.6, VI.3 and VIII.3. Stage I (D.IV.6) should show at least a circle for the head (or body) and also *at least two* other features, e.g. 2 of the following: eyes, legs, arms, nose, mouth, feet, body, hands, fingers, etc. (Fig. 27).

SCALE D. HAND AND EYE CO-ORDINATION
YEAR V

Items

D.V.1. *Draws a good cross.* Stage II. (See D.III.6). (Record Book, page 7).

At this level a good cross is expected. The upright line should be approximately perpendicular and the horizontal line

D.V.1   Drawing a good cross   Stage II

Fig. 21

should cross it at approximately a right angle. Good cross, firm lines, good shape. (Fig. 21).

D.V.2. *Draws a circle.* Stage II. (See D.III.5). (Record Book, page 7).

At this level, the circle should be a good shape and neatly closed. (Fig. 22).

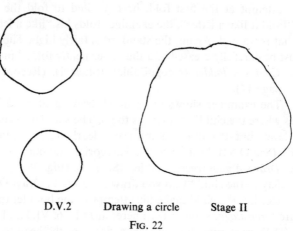

D.V.2   Drawing a circle   Stage II

FIG. 22

D.V.3. *Draws a recognisable square.* Stage I. (See also D.VII.1). Show the square in the booklet (page 14), and invite the child to try to draw one like it in the space provided. The standard at this level is lenient. The square must have 4 sides and be approximately the right shape, but exact drawing is not expected. (Fig. 23).

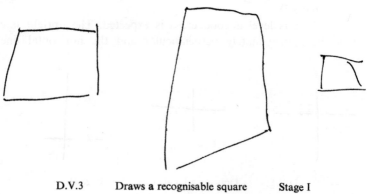

D.V.3   Draws a recognisable square   Stage I

FIG. 23

D.V.4.   *Draws a window*. Stage I. (See also D.VIII.2).

This is a combination of the square and the cross. Both must appear and the drawing must be recognisable as a window; but the standard is lenient. (Record Book, page 14). (Fig. 24).

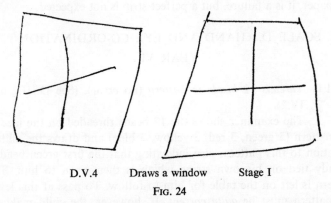

D.V.4   Draws a window   Stage I

FIG. 24

D.V.5.   *Drawing a house*. Stage I.

The examiner asks: "Can you draw a house, a nice little one, over here"– finding a place if possible on page 6 in the booklet, otherwise on page 15. Encourage the child to put into the drawing as much as he can, without instructing him what to do.

Minimum standard only expected, e.g. a rough square, with *at least two* other features: door, window, chimney, etc. (See House, Fig. 25). (See also D.VI.6 and D.VIII.7 and 8).

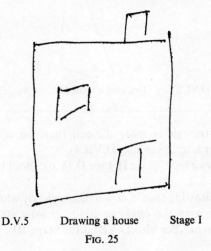

D.V.5   Drawing a house   Stage I

FIG. 25

D.V.6. *Can strip edge of paper, with scissors.* (See D.IV.3).

The examiner should again take a little square of paper and cut a strip off the edge, showing that care is needed. The child is expected to cut off a strip about a quarter of an inch or less from the edge, fairly straight. If the scissors run off the edge of the paper, it is a failure, but a perfect strip is not expected.

SCALE D. HAND AND EYE CO-ORDINATION
YEAR VI

Items

D.VI.1. *Threads* 12 *beads to pattern* (no error). (See D.III.2 and IV.2).

The examiner shows the 12 beads threaded on the lace in the pattern (3 green, 3 red, 3 yellow, 3 blue) and draws the child's attention to this pattern, also indicating that the first green bead is already tied on his own string which is then given to him. The pattern is left on the table for him to follow. To pass at this level, the pattern must be *quite correct*. If, however, the child makes a mistake, he must be allowed to continue, as his threading may credit him with a score at D.IV.2 or D.III.2.

D.VI.2. *Draws a triangle.* Stage A. (Booklet, page 14). (Fig. 26).

Standard: Recognisable shape and fairly good drawing.

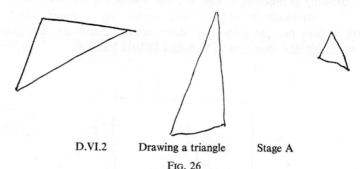

D.VI.2   Drawing a triangle   Stage A

FIG. 26

The triangle is more difficult than the square; hence its position a year later. (See also D.VII.4).

D.VI.3. *Draws a man.* Stage II. (See D.IV.6). (Booklet, page 7 or 15). (Fig. 27).

The drawing should now indicate clearly what is represented and, in addition to the circle or head, *at least six* other features should be present. (See also D.VIII.3 for Stage III).

D.IV.6   Draws a man   Stage I

Stage I

Stage II

Stage II

D.VI.3   Draws a man   Stage II

Fig. 27

D.VI.4.   *Makes at least* 3+ *letters or figures without help.* (Booklet, page 17).

The examiner asks the child if he can write his own name. The child may not be able to do this, but may make a few letters. He should in any case be encouraged to do some more writing of letters or figures, *without being shown.* He may, for example, know the first letter of his name. (See D.VI.5).

D.VI.5.   *Writes own first name.* (See also D.VII. 6).

At this stage the child is expected to be able to write – or print – his own first name. (Booklet, page 17).

D.VI.6.   *Draws a house.* Stage II. (See D.V.5). (Booklet, page 15).

The houses children draw at this stage vary considerably.

Any neatly drawn house with at least a good basic square or rectangular shape, with 5 or 6 features such as: door, window, sloping roof, chimney, steps or stairs, door knob, curtains, etc., passes at this level. If the child stops before he has completed enough to score at this level, it is legitimate to ask (without mentioning any item): "Have you finished the house?" or, "Do you want to do any more?" He may then add a feature or two that give him a pass. If he does a superior drawing, he may also pass at Stage III. (See D.VIII.7 and 8). For scoring standards and examples see Figs. 25, 30, 31, 32 and 33.

SCALE D.   HAND AND EYE CO-ORDINATION
YEAR VII

Items

D.VII.1.   *Copies a square.* Stage II. (See D.V.3). (Booklet, page 14). Superior – good shape, neatly drawn, with carefully finished corners.

D.VII.2.   *Copies a ladder.* Stage II. (See D.IV.5).

Good drawing. At least 3 rungs should be drawn, reaching but not over-running the sides. Sides straight and perpendicular. A neat model (Fig. 29).

D.VII.3.   *Draws a diamond.* Stage A. (See also VIII.4 and 5).

Show the model and where the child's attempt is to go. (Booklet, page 14). The shape should be recognisable as a diamond, having four sides, fairly neat.

D.VII.4.   *Draws a triangle.* Stage B. (See D.VI.2).

Good shape, neat drawing, sides firm and straight, corners tidy. (Booklet, page 14). Closely like the copy in Record Book, page 14).

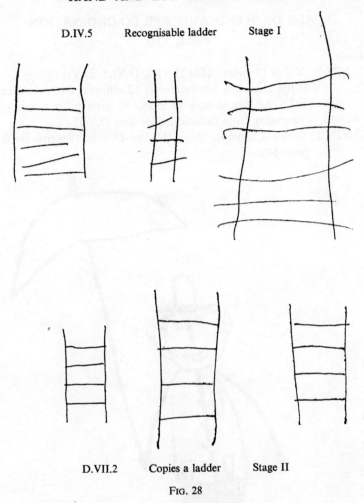

D.IV.5   Recognisable ladder   Stage I

D.VII.2   Copies a ladder   Stage II

Fig. 28

D.VII.5. *Can write figures* 1 *to* 9. (Booklet, page 17).

Ask the child: "Can you write numbers?" The ask him to write: 1, 2, 3, etc. in the space provided at the bottom of page 17 in the Record Book.

D.VII.6. *Can write full name.*

Following D.VI.5, if the child can write his first name, urge him to write his second name also, in the space left at the foot of page 17 in the record booklet.

SCALE D.   HAND AND EYE CO-ORDINATION
YEAR VIII

Items

D.VIII.1. *Makes* 12 *letters.* (See D.VI.4, D.VI.5, D.VII.6).

If the child has not produced 12 different letters in Item VII.6, he should now be asked to write more letters on page 17, if necessary from dictation. (See also D.VIII.6).

D.VIII.2. *Draws a window.* Stage II. (See D.V.4). (Record Book, page 14).

Drawing of a man   Stage III

FIG. 29

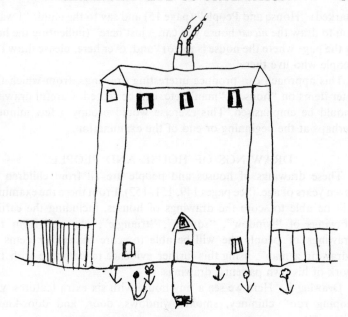

Drawing "a house" superior   Stage III

FIG. 30

Superior drawing expected at this stage, *closely like the model* on page 14.

D.VIII.3. *Drawing of a man*. Stage III. (See D.IV.6 and D.VI.3).

Superior figure expected, showing some originality, e.g.

the man should be clad, or drawn side-faced or in some attitude more difficult to draw, such as seated at table, etc. See Fig. 29 (superior model).

D.VIII.4 } *Draws a diamond*. Stage B. (See D.VII.3).

and 5. } Superior model closely like the copy in Record Book, page 14. (*Credit* as *two* items).

D.VIII.6. *Can write* 24 to 26 *letters correctly* (page 17).

(See D.VIII.1 and earlier stages).

Extra Items

D.VIII.7 } *Drawing of a house* Stage III. (See D.V.5 and D.VI.6).

and 8. } Superior model (page 15). (*Credit* as *two* items). For examples see Figs. 30, 32 and 33.

Note on the drawing of house and people:

To save time and also make these items more interesting to the older children, the examiner should turn to the page in Record Book marked: "House and People" (page 15) and say to the child: "I want you to draw the *nicest* house you can – just here" (indicating the half of the page where the house is to go) "and, over here, please draw the people who live there".

This approach can produce interesting drawings, from which the later items on "house", "man", etc. can be scored. Careful drawing should be emphasised. This exercise would occupy a few minutes perhaps at the beginning or end of the examination.

DRAWINGS OF HOUSE AND PEOPLE

These drawings of houses and people are all from children of seven years of age. (See pages 149, 151, 152). From these the examiner will be able to score the drawings of houses, including the earlier drawings of "window", "square", "triangle", etc. and from the drawings of people, he will be able to score the earlier items of "drawing a man", using this further evidence to compare with the work of his own patients' drawings.

Drawing 1. Here we see a tidy house with six extra features, viz. sloping roof, chimney, smoke, windows, door, and door-knob. (Stage II).

The people are clad, trousers are drawn with double lines showing thickness, instead of the frequent single line drawing for legs. The man has a pipe. The woman has hair ribbon and a skirt. The two children are similarly drawn. (Stage III).

Drawing 2. Again a neat house is drawn, with sloping roof, upright chimney, windows, curtains, door, number of house, knocker and letter box. The people are shown walking and are drawn *sideways* to show this. They are clad, and have caps on their heads. (House, Stage III; People, Stage III).

Drawing 3. This drawing shows the *side* of the house as well as the front. The roof is good. There are also windows, a door and a porch. The people are well clad. The man has a *tie* and a *pocket* in his shirt. The woman has a hat and *high heels* to her shoes. Both have facial features and fingers drawn. (Stage III).

All these three drawings of "house and people", are superior drawings at age 7+, and will give opportunities for scoring a number of earlier items, taken already during the examination. With clever children it is quite a good plan to let them do this picture of house and people, and it will be found that most of the items of the drawing sequence, are already present in this one effort, and need not therefore be separately tested for. The child, in all the drawing items, should be encouraged to do the best he can.

House and people 1
House: Stage II   People: Stage III

FIG. 31

House and people 2   House: Stage III   People: Stage III
                       superior drawings

Fig. 32

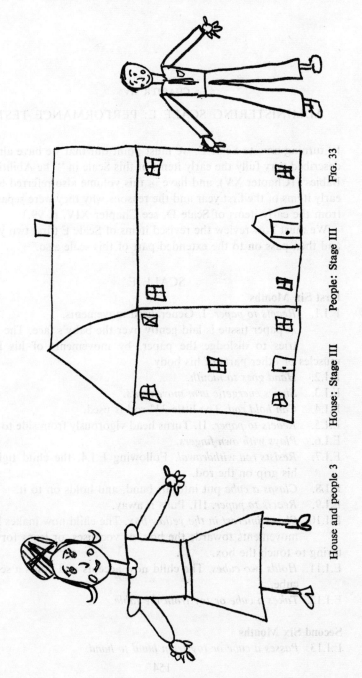

FIG. 33

People: Stage III

House: Stage III

House and people 3

ADMINISTERING SCALE E: PERFORMANCE TESTS

In turning now to Scale E, we must point out that we have already described very fully the early items of this Scale in "The Abilities of Babies" (Chapter XV), and have in this volume also referred to the early items of the first year and the reasons why they were separated from the early items of Scale D, see Chapter XIV, p. 99.

We must now review the revised items of Scale E (first two years) and then pass on to the extended part of this scale also.

SCALE E

First Six Months

E.I.1. *Reacts to paper.* I. Generalised movements.
A paper tissue is laid gently over the baby's face. The child tries to dislodge the paper, by movements of his facial muscles or other parts of his body.

E.I.2. *Hand goes to mouth.*

E.I.3. *Shows energetic arm movements.*

E.I.4. *Can hold rod.* The little $3\frac{1}{2}''$ rod is used.

E.I.5. *Reacts to paper.* II. Turns head vigorously from side to side.

E.I.6. *Plays with own fingers.*

E.I.7. *Resists rod withdrawal.* Following E.I.4, the child tightens his grip on the rod.

E.I.8. *Clasps a cube* put into his hand, and holds on to it.

E.I.9. *Reacts to paper.* III. Pulls it away.

E.I.10. *Shows interest in the yellow box.* The child now makes hand movements towards the box, or vocalises, or leans forward trying to touch the box.

E.I.11. *Holds two cubes.* The child now accepts and holds a second cube.

E.I.12. *Takes a cube or toy from the table.*

Second Six Months

E.I.13. *Passes a cube or toy from hand to hand.*

E.I.14. *Drops one cube for a third.* Whilst the child is holding a cube in each hand, he accepts a third one when offered, dropping one of the others.

E.I.15. *Manipulates two objects at once.* Two rings should be used for this or the cup and spoon, etc.

E.I.16. *Reacts to paper.* IV. Plays with the paper, waving or tearing it.

E.I.17. *Lifts inverted cup in search of toy.*

E.I.18. *Rattles the box.* The examiner rattles the box and places it near the child, who takes it up and rattles it in imitation.

E.I.19. *Lifts the lid off the box.*

E.I.20. *Clicks two bricks together.* (In imitative play).

E.I.21. *Tries to take the cubes out of the box.*

E.I.22. *Finds the toy* or cube under the cup.

E.I.23. *Accepts the third cube* without dropping. Following E.I.14 the child accepts the third cube.

E.I.24. Manipulates box, lid, and cubes in play.

Third Six Months

E.II.1. *Removes both cubes from the box*, after being shown.

E.II.2. *Unwraps and finds a toy.*

E.II.3. Form Boards I. *One circle board.*
The board is placed before the child, and the examiner places the large circle or inset in its hole, while the child watches. The inset is then taken out and placed in front of the child who is requested to put it back in again. Two trials.

E.II.4. *Opens two boxes.* Two boxes with lids on are put in front of the child who is asked to open them.

E.II.5. *Puts cubes in and out of boxes in play.*

E.II.6. *Puts two cubes back into a box.*

E.II.7. Form Boards II. *The two-circle board. One in.*
The board is placed in front of the child and the examiner puts both circles in place. He then lifts them out and places them on the table, between the child and the board. The child replaces *one* of them.

E.II.8. Form Boards III. *The Square Board.* Two trials.

E.II.9. Form Boards IV. *The Two Circle Board. Two in.*

E.II.10. *Can put the lid back on the box.*

E.II.11. Form Boards V. *Three-hole Board. One in.*

E.II.12. Puts two cubes back into box, lid on, all complete.

Fourth Six Months

E.II.13.   Form Boards VI. *Circle and square board together.*

The circle and square boards are placed together so as to form one board. Then the examiner takes out the two insets and places them near the child as before, and the child is asked to put them in again. *Both* insets must be correctly placed to pass this item.

E.II.14.   Form Boards VII. *Three Hole Board. Two in.*

As for E.II.11, but now two insets must be correctly placed.

E.II.15.   Form Boards VIII. *Three Hole Board, Three in.*

E.II.16.   Form Boards IX. *Two Circle Board Rotated.*

The examiner lifts the board slowly, leaving the two insets on the table. Then placing the board behind the insets, he requests the child to replace them.

Note: re Form Boards. It is important when taking the Form Board items with babies not to frustrate the child by beginning at the "One circle board" and expecting the child to continue throughout the whole sequence! The rule is to begin at a point two months below the child's actual age, and continue until he fails a *total* of six consecutive items of the performance series and then take no more performance items. This we have called the six-item rule and it holds throughout the entire examination in all the Scales from birth to the ninth year.

E.II.17   Form Board X. *Circle and square boards rotated.*
and 18.   (Credit as two items).

E.II.19   *Assembles all three boxes.* After a brief play session with
and 20.   the three boxes, the child is asked to put them all away.

This item is passed if the child can persist long enough to get two bricks into each box, and the lids on, irrespective of correct placement by colour.

E.II.21   *Can open the screw toy.* (Credit as two items).
and 22.

E.II.23   *Three hole board rotated.* (Credit as two items).
and 24.

Note: See also "The Abilities of Babies", p. 201.

In the Extended Scale E (see below) a number of items are included that carry the use of the "Brick Boxes" and the "Form Boards", to further more difficult items. These are fully described in the text, and the standards for scoring the *timed* items are given also in the Record Book.

The Brick Boxes. These three little wooden boxes all made to be exactly alike in size, but differing in colour, each containing two one-inch bricks, have proved versatile in the testing sequence. Used in the main in the second year of the tests, they are also useful in the third and fourth years for new items such as 'Train under bridge', 'Building a gate', etc. and are useful as far as the end of the fifth year.

The Form Boards. The three new form-boards, namely the four-squares-board, the six-hole-board, and the eleven-hole-board, provide a sequence of increasing difficulty for the whole period from three to eight years. As each one, in being administered, is timed with the stop watch, it has been possible to derive no less than eleven items of test from these three little boards. They therefore give opportunities for the study of the developing capacities of these young children.

The children also very much enjoy, the *Block Pattern Test*.

The full range of items for Scale E is listed below.

SCALE E.   PERFORMANCE

Note: Many of the Performance Items are *timed* and are credited at various levels according to the time taken, as shown in the Record Book.

These items are therefore not described more than once here, but are listed below.

Summary of Timed Tests	*Scored at:*	*Time:*
Return of nine bricks and lid to box:–	E.III.2	60 secs.
	E.IV.1	40 ,,
	E.VI.5	20 ,,
	E.VIII.4	15 ,,
Four-squares Board:–	E.III.3	60 secs.
	E.III.5	40 ,,
	E.IV.4	15 ,,
	E.VII.3	7 ,,
Six-hole Board:–	E.III.4	60 secs.
	E.III.6	40 ,,
	E.V.1	20 ,,
	E.VIII.2	10 ,,
Eleven-hole Board:–	E.IV.6	60 secs.
	E.VI.1	40 ,,
	E.VII.4	30 ,,

Pattern Making – Block Pattern Test:

Pattern No. 2	E.V.3	60 secs.
	E.V.5	40 ,,
	E.VII.5	20 ,,
	E.VIII.5	15 ,,
Pattern No. 3	E.VI.4	60 ,,
	E.VII.1	40 ,,
	E.VII.6	30 ,,
	E.VIII.6	20 ,,
Pattern No. 4	E.VI.6	60 ,,
	E.VII.2	40 ,,
	E.VIII.1	30 ,,
	E.VIII.7	20 ,,
Pattern No. 5	E.V.6	60 ,,
	E.VI.2	40 ,,
	E.VIII.3	10 ,,
	E.VIII.8	15 ,,

SCALE E.   PERFORMANCE.   YEAR III

Items

E.III.1 *Re-assembles screw toy.*

Following E.II.21, if the child, having opened the screw toy and seen the little toy inside, can also close it again, he passes E.III.1.

E.III.2 *Returns 9 bricks to box and puts the lid on.* (60 secs.).

Time by stop-watch and record the time taken. (*One* trial only).

Apparatus: square box containing 9 small brown bricks. Take the box and remove the lid. Tip out the little bricks. Say: "I want to see how quickly you can put these bricks back into this box *and put the lid on*". Say: "Ready . . . Go!" and note carefully the time taken. He must not forget the lid. Time in seeconds and enter in the appropriate places, in the Record Book.

E.III.3 *Four-squares board* (in 60 seconds).

Allow *two trials* and note the time taken.

Place the board with the *smallest* square to the child's *left* hand. Lift out the largest first and pile the squares in a pyramid, according to size, the smallest on top. Say: "I want to see if you can put all these squares back again. I am going to see how quickly you can do it". Take twice and *score the quicker attempt*. Give credit, where indicated, in the record book.

E.III.4. *Six-hole board* (in 60 seconds).

Take *twice*, timing with the stop-watch.

Place the board in front of the child with the *oval* inset *away* from him. Take out and pile up the insets, in two piles of three. Say: "I want to see if you can put all these blocks back again. See how quickly you can do it". All six insets must be placed correctly, without help.

Note the two times and score the *quicker* attempt at the appropriate levels.

E.III.5. *Four-squares board* (40 seconds). (See E.III.3).

E.III.6. *Six-hole board* (40 seconds). (See E.III.4).

SCALE E. PERFORMANCE. YEAR IV

Items

E.IV.1. *Returns 9 bricks to box, lid on*. (40 seconds). (See E.III.2).

E.IV.2. *Builds bridge with three boxes*. (See also E.IV.5 and V.2).

Bridge not necessarily superior model, but *stands*.

Take the brick-boxes and take all the pieces apart. The lids are *not* used for this item. Using the *boxes only*, place two of these upside down, side by side, with a space between. The third box, also upside down, is hung by its ridge on and between the other two. Then say: "See, this box has a little ridge all round it; this makes a good strong railway bridge". Then, taking the six bricks, make a train and send it slowly under the bridge towards the child.

The examiner asks the child to look carefully at the bridge. "Do you think *you* could make one just like that, and make the train and send it back to *my* station?" The child agrees and the bridge is then demolished, each box being turned over or on its side and the bricks mixed up. The child then tries to build the bridge and make the train go under it.

If the bridge *stands* but is *not* made by using the ridge (not correct model though it stands), he passes only E.IV.2. If it is *quite* correctly built and does not fall down when the train goes under it, he scores for both E.IV.5 and E.V.2 also.

E.IV.3. *Assembles brick-boxes by colour* (all 12 pieces).

N.B. *Before* taking this item, it is best to do other items requiring the brick-boxes, i.e. E.IV.2, IV.5, V.2 and V.4, and then score this item as the child is putting the bricks away.

Place the empty boxes in a row before the child: red,

yellow and blue, with the lids in front of the *wrong* boxes – yellow, blue and red. Then scatter the bricks nearby and say: "Can you put them away now, the red ones in the red box, the blue in the blue box and the yellow in the yellow box, and put the right lid on?"

Should the child without further help re-assemble all twelve pieces correctly for colour, he passes E.IV.3.

E.IV.4.   *Four-squares.* (15 seconds). (See E.III.3.).

E.IV.5.   *Train under bridge.* (See E.IV.2).

E.IV.6.   *Eleven-hole board* (within 60 seconds).

Give *two trials* and note the time taken.

Place the board with the *star* at the top *away* from the child. Proceed as for the six-hole board. Take out the insets and arrange them in two piles of five with the circle on top. Score the *quicker* of the child's two attempts at the appropriate levels.

SCALE E.   PERFORMANCE.   YEAR V

Items

E.V.1.   *Six-hole board* (within 20 seconds). (See E.III.4).

E.V.2.   *Builds bridge: superior model.* (See E.IV.2).

E.V.3.   *Pattern-Making.* (No. 2 in 60 seconds). *One* trial only.

Take the booklet with the Block Pattern Test and say: "I am going to see if you can make patterns". Place the booklet, open at the *first* pattern, a little distance from the child and, opening the box of nine bricks (3 red, 3 blue, 3 yellow), mix them up *to his right* and say: "Do you think you could make that pattern with these bricks, just here? See, the three red ones are at the top, then the yellow, then the blue". Show the child, if necessary. When he is ready, say: "Now you make it".

This pattern (No. 1) is used *for demonstration only* and is *not* credited.

Proceed with Patterns Nos. 2 to 5, giving no further help. Score plus if correct and minus if the pattern is wrong, and *time* with the stop-watch. Credit the time taken for each correct pattern at the appropriate place in the record book. (One trial only for each).

Note that many little children can do Nos. 2 and 5, but *not* Nos. 3 and 4 because of the influence of the diagonal pattern. If the child fails No. 3, it may be desirable to omit No. 4 and go on to No. 5, which is easier and leaves the child still encouraged.

E.V.4.   *Builds 'gate' to model, using 3 boxes and lids.*

Before the brick-boxes are put away, this item should be taken. (The bricks are not required and should be put aside). The examiner builds the 'gate' as follows: Placing all three boxes upside down in a row, with about one inch space between them, put two lids over the two spaces and the third lid on top. Then say: "Look! this is the Marble Arch" or: "This is a big gate". "Have a good look at it. The cars can go through here . . . and through here . . . and this is like a window on top. Do you think you could make it now?"

The examiner then lifts the pieces apart and places them overturned at random on the table, and the child tries to build it. Score plus if correct model.

E.V.5.   Pattern-making No. 2. (40 seconds).
E.V.6.   Pattern-making No. 5. (60 seconds).

SCALE E.   PERFORMANCE.   YEAR VI

Items

E.VI.1.   *Eleven-hole board.* (40 seconds).
E.VI.2.   Pattern-making No. 5. (40 seconds).
E.VI.3.   *Ten-brick memory stairs.*
        Take ten yellow bricks and say: "Now, look what I am going to do. See! I am making a stair-case".

The examiner builds a stair of ten bricks, and draws the child's attention by pretending to let the finger (or a tiny doll) walk, as it were, up the stairs.

        "Do you think that you could build the stairs like that?" Demolish the stairs and let the child try. Score plus if correct.

    (The remaining items in Year VI, and all those in Years VII and VIII, are *timed* tests. The method in each case is given above).

E.VI.4.   Pattern-making No. 3. (60 seconds).
E.VI.5.   Returns nine bricks to box, and replaces lid. (20 seconds).
E.VI.6.   Pattern-making No. 4. (60 seconds).
E.VII.1. Pattern-making No. 3. (40 seconds).
E.VII.2. Pattern-making No. 4. (40 seconds).
E.VII.3. Four-squares board. (7 seconds).
E.VII.4. Eleven-hole board. (30 seconds).
E.VII.5. Pattern-making No. 2. (20 seconds).
E.VII.6. Pattern-making No. 3. (30 seconds).
E.VIII.1. Pattern-making No. 4. (30 seconds).
E.VIII.2. Six-hole board (within 10 seconds).
E.VIII.3. Pattern-making No. 5. (20 seconds).
E.VIII.4. Returns nine bricks to box, plus lid (within 15 seconds).
E.VIII.5. Pattern-making No. 2. (15 seconds).

E.VIII.6. Pattern-making No. 3. (20 seconds).
E.VIII.7. Pattern-making No. 4. (20 seconds).
E.VIII.8. Pattern-making No. 5. (15 seconds).

Pattern-making: For details of the method of administering the Pattern-making items, see E.V.3, p. 160.

Note: Turning now to Scale F, we begin with item F.III.1 and continue to item F.VIII.8.

There are no items in Scale F (Practical Reasoning) below the third year. (See p. 39).

CHAPTER XVI

NOTES ON ADMINISTERING THE
PRACTICAL REASONING SCALE (F)

For a full note on Scale F the reader is referred to Chapter VI,
Section on Scale F "Practical Reasoning" (page 39)

SCALE F. PRACTICAL REASONING. YEAR III

Items

F.III.1. *Repeats 1 digit.* (8; 2; 7). (See also F.III.3 and F.III.5).

Say to the child: "I am going to say numbers. I want you
to say them when I've finished. Now listen. Say '8'."

If the child does not respond, say '2' – then '7'.

If he will repeat one number correctly, score plus for F.III.1, then
go on to two digits (F.III.3).

One correct result is sufficient to give him his mark at this (and
each) level.

F.III.2. *Knows 'penny' or 'money'.* (See also F.V.1).

The examiner should produce a penny and place it before
the child and ask "What is this?" . . . "Tell me what we
call it". If he answers "penny" or "money", this is sufficient at this
stage.

Note: If the child has already named the penny in item C.III.1
where a penny is one of the twelve objects, F.III.2 can be
omitted and scored plus.

F.III.3. *Repeats 2 digits.* (5-3; 1-6; 9-4).

Take as for F.III.1. If one pair of numbers is correct, go on
to F.III.5.

F.III.4. *Compares two insets for size.* (See also F.III.6).

Apparatus: The two circular insets from the two-circle
board). Attract the child's attention by clicking the two
insets together, then place them before him on the table and say:
"One of these is *bigger* than the other. *Which* is the bigger one?"
If he touches the bigger one, *make no comment* but change the
position of the pieces in relation to each other and again say:
"One of these is bigger than the other. Which is the bigger one?"

If the child is right *both times*, score this item plus. (Then go on to F.III.6).

F.III.5.   *Repeats* 3 *digits*. (9-8-2; 4-7-5; 1-3-6).

Take as for F.III.1. *One* correct is sufficient.

See also F.IV.5 (four digits), F.VI.4 (five digits).

F.III.6.   Knows '*big*' and '*little*'. (See F.III.4).

Following F.III.4, touching the insets, first the big one and then the little one, say: "This one is big, and this one is . . ?" Note what the child says, ('little' or 'small'). Any suitable opposite to 'big' is scored plus.

SCALE F.   PRACTICAL REASONING.   YEAR IV

Items

F.IV.1.   *Compares two towers*. (See also F.VI.6).

"Which is the higher tower?" (3 or 5 bricks).

Take the yellow bricks and quickly build two towers, one of 5 bricks and one of 3. Say to the child: "Here are two towers. One of these is *higher* than the other. *Which* is the higher one?" If the child responds correctly, change the position of the towers and ask again: "Which is the higher one?" If he responds *both times* correctly, he passes F.IV.1. (Go straight on to F.VI.6).

F.IV.2.   *Compares two lines for length*. (See also F.VII.6).

Show the appropriate drawing (in the Record Book p. 13) of the two lines, saying: "One of these lines is *longer* than the other. *Which* is the longer one?" If the child responds correctly, make no comment, turn the drawing round so as to reverse the position of the lines, and ask again: "Which is the longer one?" The child must respond correctly *both times* to score plus for F.IV.2.

The examiner may *draw* two lines for the child if he seems not to understand. (Some three-year olds do not know the word "line").

F.IV.3.   *Preliminary counting to* 4+.

Children of these ages frequently learn the early sequence of numbers and can *repeat* these to about 5 or 6 in the right order, but they may be quite unable to count objects correctly. This preliminary counting, which involves memorising a sequence of numbers, is necessary as a stage in the child's understanding of the numerical sequence and it scores plus at this level. (F.IV.3).

F.IV.4.   *Can count* 4 *bricks correctly*. (See also F.V.2).

Place four yellow bricks in a row before the child, not touching, but about one inch apart. Ask: "Can you count these? How many are there?" The child should touch each brick with the forefinger, and his counting must keep pace with his finger. When he has finished, say: "How many was that?" If he knows, score plus. If he does not know, give a second trial. (Some children say the numerical sequence but associate it incorrectly with the objects).

F.IV.5.   *Repeat 4 digits.* (5-8-1-6; 3-7-2-9; 4-9-5-2). See F.III.5).
Again, *one* series is sufficient to pass.

F.IV.6.   *Compares two weights.* (See also F.VIII.4).
Apparatus: 2 circular weights.

Ask the child to hold out his hands, palms upwards, then gently and simultaneously place the little weights one on each hand, resting partly on his fingers, where they join the palm. Say: "One of these is *heavier* than the other. *Which* is the heavier one?"

Take the weights and (behind the back) reverse them and again put them on the child's upturned hands, repeating the question. The child must be right *both times* to score plus.

Then, pointing to the heavier one, say: "This one is *heavy*, and this is . . .?" (The child must reply "light" to pass F.VIII.4).

SCALE F.   PRACTICAL REASONING.   YEAR V

Items

F.V.1.   *Knows 2 coins.* (See also F.V.4, F.VI.2 & 3, F.VIII.2 & 6).
Have the seven coins in a box. Spread them out at random in front of the child and say: "This is money. Do you know the names of our money?" If the child hesitates, point to the penny and say: "What is this? What do we call it?" If he does not repond, say: "It's a penny, isn't it?" The child assents. Then say: "Tell me some of the others. What is this one?" etc. Note those correctly named and the number failed, and credit accordingly, here and at subsequent levels.

F.V.2.   *Can count 10 bricks.* (See also F.V.6.)
As for F.IV.4, but this time placing *ten* yellow bricks in the row, not quite touching each other. "How many have I put there? Go on, you count these bricks". When he has finished, ask: "How many was that?" If he does not know, give a second trial. If he is right, he passes both F.V.2 and F.IV.4. If he fails, give only 4 bricks and see if he can count them and so pass F.IV.4, if that item was not done first.

F.V.3.   *Knows morning and afternoon.*
Ask: "Is this the morning or the afternoon?" putting *first* the *correct* answer, i.e. in the morning say as above; in the afternoon, say: "Is this the afternoon or the morning?"

F.V.4.   *Knows* 3 *coins.* (As for F.V.1).

F.V.5.   *"Which goes faster?"*

Ask: "Which goes faster, a big boy running or a little boy running?"

"Which goes faster, a bird flying or an aeroplane?"

"Which goes faster, a car or a bicycle?"

All three questions must be correctly answered to score plus for F.V.5.

F.V.6.   *Can count* 15 *bricks.*

If the child has counted ten bricks correctly (F.V.2), take five more and add them to the row. Let him count the fifteen if he can. When he has finished, say: "How many was that?" As before, he must give the total number correctly.

SCALE F. PRACTICAL REASONING.   YEAR VI

Items

F.VI.1.   *Knows number of fingers on each hand.* (See also F.VI.5).

(a)   Take the child's right hand and, holding it gently closed, to prevent counting, say: "How many fingers have you on this hand, counting the thumb?" Score plus or minus.

(b)   Then taking the left hand, do the same, and score. If these answers are correct, take *both* hands gently together and ask: "How many is that altogether?" A correct response scores plus for F.VI.5 also.

F.VI.2.   *Names* 4 *coins.* (See F.V.1).

F.VI.3.   *Names* 5 *coins.* (See F.V.1).

F.VI.4.   *Repeats* 5 *digits.* (6-1-3-8-4; 5-9-7-2-1; 9-2-7-8-6). (See also F.III.1, 3 and 5, and F.IV.5).

F.VI.5.   *Knows number of fingers on both hands.* Counting is not allowed. (5+5=10). (See F.VI.1).

F.VI.6.   *Knows 'high' and 'low'.* (See F.IV. 1).

If the child indicates correctly which is the higher tower, continue by pointing and by asking: "This one is high, then this one is . . . ?" The only acceptable answer is "low".

SCALE F. PRACTICAL REASONING.   YEAR VII

Items

F.VII.1.   *Can count up to* 30.

At this stage the child may be permitted just to count, saying the numbers of the sequence without reference to any objects.

F.VII.2. *Knows right and left:* (8).

(Right hand, Left ear, Right foot, Right eye;
Left hand, Right ear, Left foot, Left eye).

Take this *item slowly*. Facing the child, say: "Which is your right hand? Hold up your right hand". "Which is your left ear? Show me your left ear". Similarly with the others, in the order given above. *All eight* must be correct to score plus. The examiner should avoid looking towards the part of the body when naming it, and should avoid betraying whether the child is right or not.

F.VII.3. *Can count backwards from* 10. (See also F.VIII.5).

Say: "Can you count backwards? Listen: Begin with 10 and count downwards until you get to 1. Can you do that?"

Allow two trials. This must be *quite correct* to score plus.

F.VII.4. *Can say the days of the week.* (See also F.VIII.1).

Ask: "Do you know the names of all the days of the week?

Say them for me". If the child hesitates or appears not to understand, say: "You know, begin with Sunday . . ." If he says the days in their right order, say: "That's right", then "What comes after Thursday? . . . What comes before Tuesday?"

Naming all the days correctly scores plus at VII.4. Answering both questions correctly scores at F.VIII.1.

F.VII.5. *Tells the time: hours only.* (4 o'clock).

Produce the clock face and say: "Can you tell the time?

Well, we'll see". Set the clock, turned away from the child, at 4 o'clock and show it to the child, asking: "What time does this clock say?" The correct response scores plus at F.VII.5.

If correct, set the clock at 8.30 and repeat the question (F.VIII.7). Finally, set it at 10.45 (F.VIII.8).

F.VII.6. *Knows 'long' and 'short'.* (See F.IV.2).

Following F.IV.2, if the child passed at that level, the examiner now points first to the longer line and then to the shorter one, saying: "This line is long, so this line is . . .?" The only correct answer is "short".

SCALE F. PRACTICAL REASONING. YEAR VII

Items

F.VIII.1. *Days of the week.* (2 questions).

Following F.VII.4, ask the two questions as set out: "What comes after Thursday?". . ."What comes before Tuesday?" Both question correctly answered scores plus.

F.VIII.2. *Names 6 coins correctly.* (See F.V.1 and 4, F.VI.2 and 3).

F.VIII.3. *Says 3 digits backwards.* (1-8-6; 7-2-3; 4-9-3).

Say: "I am going to say some numbers and I want you to say them *backwards*. You will begin with the last one I say. Listen: 1 8 6". These should be said fairly *slowly*, at a speed of about one per second. The child needs to say only *one* of the sets of three correctly *backwards* to get his plus mark.

F.VIII.4. *Knows 'heavy' and 'light'.* (See F.IV.6).

F.VIII.5. *Can count backwards from* 20.

Take as for F.VII.3.

F.VIII.6. *Knows all 7 coins and names them correctly.* (See F.VIII.2).

Extra Items

F.VIII.7. *Tells the time: half-hours.* (8.30).

F.VIII.8. *Tells the time: quarter-hours.* (10.45).

Take as for F.VII.5.

SCORING THE NEW SCALES

(a) *For a quick total assessment* (see p. 170).

For the First Two Years

There are in the new arrangement *ten* items for each *month* of age throughout the first two years. The scoring throughout is therefore done in *months*. The examiner should count up all the items passed in the five scales, and, *dividing by ten*, will have the *total* M.A. for the first two years in months.

For the Years III to VIII+

Throughout these six years of the tests there are 36 items for each year of life including Scale F, i.e. *three* for each *month*. For the *total* M.A. credit, therefore, the examiner should *divide* the total number of items passed *by three:* the result will give the child's M.A. credit for these six years in months, including the twelve extra items at the end of Year VIII which really belong to Year IX.

The *total M.A.* for the whole range will then be arrived at by adding the M.A. credit for the first two years and the M.A. credit for the rest of the Scale, so far as the child has gone.

Then $\dfrac{\text{M.A.}}{\text{C.A.}} \times 100 =$ Total G.Q. (Total General Quotient).

(b) *Profile. Where more detailed information is required (differential diagnosis) a profile should be prepared*

For the First Two Years

For *each* of the five sub-scales A to E in the first two years, the examiner should count up the items passed, entering these in the places provided in the record book. See Summary of Test Results, page 00. There are 24 items in each of the sub-scales in each year. These sub-totals should therefore be *divided by two* (as there are two items for each month when the scales are thus taken separately). This will give the M.A. credits for each of the sub-scales.

For the Years III to VIII+

Where the child's successes go *beyond* the second year, each item within each sub-scale carries *two months* of M.A. credit. This is so throughout the whole of the Extension inlcuding the extra items. Thus there are 6 items for each year in each scale, plus the two extra items in each scale for Year IX referred to above. The number of items passed in each scale should be entered in the places provided, on the summary of tests, p. 170. If then these scores are separately *multiplied by two*, the results give the M.A. credits in months for each scale.

By adding to these the M.A. credits on each scale for the first two years, the child's *total* credits in months are arrived at for each sub-scale. This provides the necessary information for the profile.

Special Note on Scale F

Owing to the nature of the items in Scale F, this scale cannot be assessed below Year III. If, however, the older child has passed all the second year items in the five scales, two years can be assumed as his basic credit for Scale F also.

When, however, a three or four years old child (or older) has failed some items in Year II or lower, the *basic credit* for Scale F is obtained by taking the *average* M.A. credit obtained for the five scales for the first two years only. This obviates the necessity for assuming a total basic two years for Scale F which would be un-justified in such a case, and it also avoids the necessity of regarding the child as "untestable" on Scale F. In many such cases a few items are passed in all six scales in Year III and sometimes beyond.

Profile. The profile is finally obtained by dividing each of the sub-scale M.A. credits by the C.A. and multiplying by 100, to obtain the separate sub-quotients.

The final G.Q. will be the *average* of these six separately obtained quotients.

See "Summary of Test Results", p. 170.

SUMMARY OF TEST RESULTS

M.A. Credits in Months:

Summary in Months

Scales:	A	B	C	D	E	F

	A	B	C	D	E	F
YEARS I						
II						
III						
IV						
V						
VI						
VII						
VIII						
Extra Months						
Total M.A.'s (months)						
C.A. (months)						
Sub-Quotients $\dfrac{\text{M.A.'s} \times 100}{\text{C.A.}}$						

Scales A to F	Months
I $\dfrac{\text{........ items passed}}{10}$	=
II $\dfrac{\text{........ items}}{10}$	=
III $\dfrac{\text{........ items}}{3}$	=
IV $\dfrac{\text{........ items}}{3}$	=
V $\dfrac{\text{........ items}}{3}$	=
VI $\dfrac{\text{........ items}}{3}$	=
VII $\dfrac{\text{........ items}}{3}$	=
VIII $\dfrac{\text{........ items}}{3}$	=
Extras $\dfrac{\text{........ items}}{3}$	=
Total M.A. (months)	=
C.A. (months)	=
G.Q.	

Note: The General Quotient or G.Q. is obtained by taking the average of all the six sub-quotients.

Examiner's Report:

FIG. 34

170

CHAPTER XVII

CONCLUSION

In conclusion the writer would like to draw the attention of those who have read so far, to the problem of the future in this matter of mental assessment, with particular reference to the needs, in the test situation, of handicapped children and young people.

The work of building up and standardising a complicated series of tests takes many years to complete, and yet it would seem that it is far better to have available several parallel scales of tests, each measuring *a different avenue of learning*, and yet all of them equal in difficulty and standardised on the same representative populations, to provide a reliable profile, than to have what most psychologists have to use, namely, a battery of tests for different purposes, designed by different people from different points of view, with varying reliability.

It would seem that the profile technique described in the foregoing pages, might be extended along similar lines to provide adequate test procedures for children over eight years of age, up to at least the end of the usual school career, and even to adult level. If also these separate scales were suitably expanded to fulfil more completely their several functions, older children and young people, both normal and handicapped, could be more adequately catered for in this matter of mental diagnosis, or assessment, and even in the matter of future careers!

The subjects of the school curriculum fall into several groups not unlike those envisaged for this further extension of the scales. So wide now are the curricula that no child can excel at *all* the subjects taught and specialisation must take place sooner or later.

It may not be stretching the point too far to suggest that the Locomotor Scale of the future might help to discover the potential *athlete*. Personal-Social growth and development with its interest in other people, and in human welfare, might well provide the clue for entry into one of the professions such as *Medicine* or *Social Work*. The young person expert at language studies may go on naturally to learning and teaching his own and foreign languages. (Scale C).

The second half of the profile so far as it goes at present can hint at the practical and technical aspects, and *if suitably expanded* might well help a young person to find the right career, as artist perhaps, or architect, scientist or mathematician.

To undertake to extend the present scales would be a very big task, quite beyond what could be achieved by one person, however dedicated, and however assisted by voluntary part-time helpers. What is needed is a large scale investigation, at a national level, which would result in help for the handicapped on a large scale, and a wide reaching and better understanding of the problems of youth.

But these are mere speculations at the present time, and meanwhile we have in our midst handicapped children of many types, who because of their disabilities cannot hope to find the field for which their true potentialities might have fitted them. For these children the tests, as described in this book, are the most helpful, if used while the children are still very young. By means of the profile as now presented, the deaf child, the visually defective, and the child slow of development, for whatever cause, can be thoroughly investigated. The function of the mental test administered at an early age is to help to discover the cause of retardation and get the slow child seen by the relevent specialists at the earliest possible time.

Thus the deaf baby can learn very early to use a hearing aid, the child with visual difficulties can get maximum help, and the cerebral palsied child can benefit from a better understanding of his problems by those most concerned, and an education suited to his needs.

The reader may like now, in this connection, to refer to the diagram showing the Basic Avenues of Learning, as studied from earliest infancy onwards. For this see "The Abilities of Babies", page 29.

BIBLIOGRAPHY

AINSWORTH, M. D. and BOSTON, M. (1952): "Psychodiagnostic Assessment of a Child after prolonged separation in Early Childhood". Brit. J. Med. Psych. 25, 169-201.

ARMSTRONG, M. D., YATES, K. N. and CONNELLY, J. P. (1964): "Amino-acid excretion of new-born infants, during the first 24 hours of life". Paediatrica 33, 975.

BAYLEY, N. (1940): "Mental growth in young children". Year Book. Nat. Soc. Stud. Educ. 39 (II) 11-47.

BAYLEY, N. (1933): "Mental growth during the first three years. A developmental study of 61 children by repeated tests". Genetic Psychology Monographs. 14, 1-92.

BIRCH, H. D. (Ed.) (1964): "Brain damage in children; the Biological and Social Aspects". Baltimore: Williams and Williams.

BOBATH, Karel (1966): "The Motor Deficit in Patients with Cerebral Palsy". Published by the Spastics Society Medical Education and Information Unit in association with Wm. Heinemann Medical Books Ltd., London.

BRAIN, Lord R. (1961): "Speech Disorders: Aphasia, Apraxia and Agnosia". London: Butterworth.

BRERETON, Beatrice LeGay and SATTLER, Jennifer (1967): "Cerebral Palsy: Basic Abilities". The Spastic Centre of New South Wales, Mosman, N.S.W., Australia.

BRIDGES, K. M. B. (1931): "The Social and Emotional Development of the Pre-School Child". London: Kegan Paul.

BRIDGES, K. M. B. (1932): "Emotional Development in Early Infancy". Child Development 3, 324-41.

BUHLER, C. (1930): "The First Year of Life". New York: Day & Co.

BUHLER, C. (1935): "From Birth to Maturity". London: Kegan Paul.

BURT, C.: "The Subnormal Mind" (1937). Oxford University Press.

BURT, C.: "Mental and Scholastic Tests" (1921). P. S. King & Sons.

BURT, C.: "The Backward Child". (1937).

CAMERON, K., LEWIS, M. and STONE, F. H. (1961): "Is there a syndrome of brain damage in children". Cerebral Palsy Bull. 3, 74, 75, 76 (Letters).

CATTELL, P. (1940): "The Measurement of Intelligence in Infants and Young Children". (New York: The Psychological Corporation, Lancaster Pa. Sc. Press).

CREAK, Mildred (1964): "Psychosis in Childhood" being Chapter 3 in Section 2 of "The Foundations of Child Psychiatry". Edited by Emanuel Miller.

173

CREAK, Mildred *et al.* (1961): "Schizophrenic Syndrome in Childhood". "Progress Report of a Working Party". Cerebral Palsy Bull., 3, 501.

CROSSE, V. M. (1945): "The Premature Baby". London: J. & A. Churchill.

DUNSDON, M. I. (1952): "The Educability of Cerebral Palsied Children". (Newnes: London).

EWING, A. W. G. (1930): "Aphasia in Children". (Oxford University Press).

EWING, J. R. (1943): "Deafness in Infancy and Early Childhood". Journ. Laryng and Oto., 58, 4.

EWING, J. R. and EWING, A. W. G. (1938): "Handicap of Deafness". (London: Longman's Green).

EWING, J. R. and EWING, A. W. G. (1944): "Ascertainment of Deafness in Infancy and Early Childhood". J. Laryng & Oto. 59. 9.

EWING, J. R. and EWING, A. W. G. (1947): "Opportunity and the Deaf Child". University of London Press.

FLINT, Betty M. (1966): "The Child and the Institution. A Study of Deprivation and Recovery". University of Toronto Press.

GESELL, A. (1925): "The Mental Growth of the Pre-School Child". New York: MacMillan.

GESELL, A. (1942): "The First Five Years of Life". Methuen, London.

GESELL, A. and AMATRUDA, C. S. (1941): "Developmental Diagnosis: Normal and Abnormal Development". Hoeber, New York.

GESELL, A. and AMES, L. B. (1950): "Tonic-neck Reflex and Symmetro-tonic behaviour. Developmental and clinical behaviour". J. Pediat. 36, 165.

GRIFFITHS, Ruth (1933): "Children's Phantasies". Australian Journal of Psychology.

GRIFFITHS, Ruth (1935): "Imagination in Early Childhood". (London: Kegan Paul).

GRIFFITHS, Ruth (1954, 1960, 1967): "The Abilities of Babies". University of London Press.

GRIFFITHS, Ruth: "The Psycho-Diagnostic Approach to Problems of the Very Young". Being Ch. VII of "Foundations of Child Psychiatry". Editor: Emanuel Miller. Pergamon Press (1968).

ILLINGWORTH, R. S. (1966): "The Development of the Infant and Young Child, Normal and Abnormal". Edinburgh: Livingstone.

INGRAM, T. T. S. (1964): "Late and Poor Talkers". Little Club Clinics in Developmental Medicine No. 13. London. Spastics Society. Heinemann.

ISAACS, S. (1929): "The Nursery Years". London: Routledge.

ISAACS, S. (1930, 1938): "Intellectual Growth in Young Children". Routledge, London.

ISAACS, Susan (1933): "Social Development in Young Children". London, Routledge & Kegan and Paul.

KOUPERNIK, C. (1951): "Psychiatrie Sociale de l'Enfant". (Conférence publiée sons la direction de C. Koupernik, travaux et documents du Centre International de l'Enfances, Paris).

LANGAN, I. W. (1945): Instruction Booklet for a Special Adaptation for the Blind of the 1937 Revision of the Stanford-Binet Tests. (Bristol – Stoke Park Colony).

LEWIS, M. M. (1936): "Infant Speech: A Study of the Beginnings of Language". (London: Kegan Paul).

MELCHER, R. T. (1934): "Children's Motor Learning with and without Vision". 5 – 315 – 50.

MILLER, Emanuel (Editor) with the collaboration of several authors, "Foundations of Child Psychiatry". Pergamon Press (1968).

MILLER, Emanuel: "The Problem of Classification in Child Psychiatry", being Chapter 11, in Section I, "Foundations of Child Psychiatry". Pergamon Press, 1968.

MOORE, Terence: "The Place of Longitudinal Research in the Study of Child Development", being Chapter VIII of "Foundations of Child Psychiatry". Editor: Emanuel Miller. Pergamon Press.

MURPHY, K. (1964): "Development of Normal Vocalisation and Sound" in "Little Club Clinics in Developmental Medicine", No. 13. London Spastics Society. Heinemann.

RENFREW, Catherine and MURPHY, Kevin (1964): "The Child who does not talk". Published by the Spastics Society, Medical Education and Information Unit, in association with Wm. Heinemann Medical Books Ltd., London.

ROBERTS J. A. FRASER, An Introduction to Medical Genetics; Oxford Medical Publications, Fifth Edition, 1970.

ROBERTS, J. A. F., NORMAN, R. M. and GRIFFITHS, R. (1935): "Studies on a Child Population I. Definition of the Sample, etc." Annals of Eugenics, 6, 319-38.

ROBERTS, J. A. F. and GRIFFITHS, R. (1937): "Studies on a Child Population II". "Re-tests on the Advanced Otis and Stanford-Binet Scales etc." Annals of Evgenics 8 (1), 15-45.

ROBERTS, J. A. F., NORMAN, R. M. and GRIFFITHS, R. (1938a): "Studies on a Child Population III. Intelligence and Family Size". Annals of Evgenics 8 (II), 178-215.

ROBERTS, J. A. F., NORMAN, R. M. and GRIFFITHS, R. (1938b): "Studies on a Child Population IV. The form of the lower end of the frequency distribution". Annals of Eugenics 8 (IV), 319-36.

ROBERTS, J. A. F., GORDON, R. G. and GRIFFITHS, R. (1939): "Does Poliomyelitis affect Intellectual Capacity?". B.M. Journal.

SCHONELL, F. (1942): "Backwardness in the Basic Subjects". Oliver & Boyd, Edinburgh.

SETH, G. and GUTHRIE, D. (1935): "Speech in Childhood". Oxford University Press.

SHERIDAN, Mary D. (1948): "The Child's Hearing for Speech". Methuen, London.

SHERIDAN, Mary D. (1960): "Developmental Progress of Infants and Young Children". London H.M. Stationery Office.

SHIRLEY, M. M. (1933): "The First Two Years: A Study of 25 Babies". Vols. I-III. (Minneapolis: University of Minnesota Press).

SPEARMAN, C. (1904): "General Intelligeance Objectively Determined and Measured". Amer. Journ. of Psychology. 15 (201-92).

SPEARMAN, C. (1923): "The Nature of Intelligence and the Principles of Cognition". (MacMillan, London).

SPEARMAN, C. (1927): "The Abilities of Man: Their Nature and Measurement". (MacMillan, London).

STANFORD-BINET Intelligence Scale, Manual for the Third Edition Form L.M. Lewis M. Terman and Maud A. Merrill. George G. Harrap & Co., 1961.

TERMAN, L. M. and MERRILL, M. A. (1937): "Measuring Intelligence: A Guide to the Administration of the new revised Stanford-Binet Tests of Intelligence". Houghton, Mifflin, Boston.

VALENTINE, C. W. (1942): "The Psychology of Early Childhood". (London: Methuen).

VALENTINE, C. W. (1945): "Intelligence Tests for Children". (London, Methuen).

VERNON, P. E. (1950): "The Structure of Human Abilities". (London, Methuen).

WALLIN, J. E. W. (1949): "Children with Mental and Physical Handicaps". New York: Prentice, Hall.

WHETNALL, Edith M. S., F.R.C.S. and FRY, D. B. 1964: "The Deaf Child". Wm. Heinemann Medical Books Ltd.

WOOLF, L. I., GRIFFITHS, R. and MONCRIEFF, A. (1955): "Treatment of Phenylketonuria with a Diet low in Phenylalanine". Brit. Med. Journal 1, 57.

WOOLF, L. I., GRIFFITHS, R., MONCRIEFF, A., COATES, S. and DILLISTONE, F. (1958): "The Dietary Treatment of Phenylketonuria". Archives, Diseases of Childhood. 33.

WORSTER-DROUGHT, C. (1956): "Congenital Suprabulbar Paresis". J. Laryngol. 70, 453.

INDEX